HeadStart
primary

Science

Scaled Score
Progress Tests
AND
Topic Tests

Year 3

Written by Joe White

Acknowledgements:

Author: Joe White

Editors: Laura Sumner, Peter Sumner

Cover and Page Designs: Jerry Fowler, Charlene Pilkington and Kathryn Webster

HeadStart
primary

HeadStart Primary Ltd
Elker Lane
Clitheroe
BB7 9HZ

T. 01200 423405
E. info@headstartprimary.com
www.headstartprimary.com

Published by HeadStart Primary Ltd 2019 © **HeadStart Primary Ltd 2019**

A record for this book is available from the British Library -
ISBN: 978-1-908767-83-7

Book Contents

Teachers' Notes

Scaled Score Progress Tests

Pupil Versions

Progress Test A
Progress Test B
Progress Test C

Answer Versions

Progress Test A
Progress Test B
Progress Test C

Topic Tests

Pupil Versions

Plants
Animals, including humans
Rocks
Light
Forces and magnets

Answer Versions

Plants
Animals, including humans
Rocks
Light
Forces and magnets

CD-ROM Contents

Digital versions of each Progress Test in black & white **AND** in colour
Digital versions of each Topic Test in black & white **AND** in colour
National curriculum links for each Progress Test
National curriculum links for each Topic Test
Scaled score conversion tables for each Progress Test
Standardisation tables for each Topic Test

HeadStart
primary

HeadStart primary

Science

Scaled Score Progress Tests AND Topic Tests - Teachers' Notes

Introduction - about the Progress Tests

The **HeadStart Science Scaled Score Progress Tests** have been developed to help teachers assess children's progress against the **Science National Curriculum Programme of Study Statutory Requirements**.

There are three tests: A, B and C. This provides schools with the opportunity to track progress across the school year. Tracking points may be at the end of term or at other times during the school year, depending on the preference of each school.

Each test assesses objectives from the topic-based programmes of study; all the objectives are covered across the three tests. As 'Working scientifically' should be taught using practical scientific methods, processes and skills through the teaching of the year group topics, it is expected that assessment of this aspect is mainly carried out through practical lessons.

HeadStart provides national curriculum links grids which cross reference each question against the objectives within the national curriculum statutory requirements. **These grids are available on the CD-ROM/digital version**.

The tests have been extensively trialled in schools to provide standardised scaled score tables for each test, so that a child's raw score can be converted to a standardised scaled score. **These are available on the CD-ROM/digital version.**

i

Assessment for Learning - using the information from the Progress Tests

Scaled score conversion tables (**these and rationale available on the CD-ROM/digital version**):

- enable each child's performance to be compared to the performance of other children taking the same test.
- enable comparisons of performance across all three year group tests, and across year groups, irrespective of individual test difficulty or number of questions, etc.
- provide a summative assessment of children, groups and whole class performance against the national curriculum objectives.

National curriculum links grids (**these and rationale available on the CD-ROM/digital version**):

- can identify performance against the objectives within the statutory requirements programmes of study.
- support diagnostic assessment for individual children and whole classes so that subsequent learning needs can be identified.

It is important to note that the tests provide a *guide* for teachers in assessing children's progress which should be used in conjunction with ongoing teacher assessment.

Introduction - about the Topic Tests

The **HeadStart Science Topic Tests** have been developed to provide schools with the opportunity to assess children's understanding of each topic.

These tests feature the same or similar questions as the Progress Tests, but they are organised to provide one test per topic. National curriculum links grids, which cross reference each question against the national curriculum objectives, are also available on the CD-ROM/digital version.

Standardisation information, using the results of HeadStart's extensive school-based trials for the Progress Tests, is available on the CD-ROM/digital version.

Assessment for Learning - using the information from the Topic Tests

Standardisation tables (**these and rationale available on the CD-ROM/digital version**):

- enable each child's performance to be compared to the expected standard.
- provide formative assessment of children, groups and whole class performance against the national curriculum objectives.
- provide summative information, which can be used to compare children's progress at the end of each year.

Assessment for Learning - using the information from the Topic Tests

(continued)

National curriculum links grids **(these and rationale available on the CD-ROM/digital version)**:

- can identify performance against the objectives within the statutory requirements programmes of study.
- support diagnostic assessment for individual children and whole classes so that subsequent learning needs can be identified.

It is important to note that the tests provide a *guide* for teachers in assessing children's progress which should be used in conjunction with ongoing teacher assessment.

Administration - how to manage the tests

Format

There are black & white and colour versions available for each test. The tests are designed so that they can be printed in black & white. The colour versions can be used for whiteboard use, if required.

Each test is NOT strictly timed and children should be allowed to finish or complete as much of the test as they are able. For younger children, it may be appropriate to split each test into parts and/or the class into groups.

Equipment

Each pupil will need a pencil. A ruler may also be useful.

The use of a rubber may also be appropriate in line with school policy.

Assistance

As this is a science test and not reading, it is acceptable to read the questions to pupils. Particularly for Years 1 and 2, it may be appropriate to use the CD-ROM/digital version in conjunction with a whiteboard to display and read the test to a class or group of children. However, explanations of scientific terms should not normally be given.

It is also acceptable for children to have an amanuensis, if this is usual classroom practice. If pupils have a specific need, they should be provided with arrangements in line with normal classroom practice.

Administering the tests

For older children, check that seating is appropriately spaced and no pupil can see another pupil's answer sheet. For younger children, it may be appropriate to conduct the tests in groups or even individually.

Marking the tests and generating the scaled scores and standardisation tables

Mark the tests according to the answer version / mark scheme provided. For questions which require written responses, teachers' judgement may be required, as detailed below:

- For some questions, the mark scheme indicates 'Answer should suggest...' This means that the teacher can accept an appropriate age-related response which identifies the correct answer.

- Where the mark scheme indicates several answers separated by a forward slash, only one of the answers is needed for the child to be awarded the mark.

- For some questions, the mark scheme indicates possible answers using 'e.g....' and '(Accept other appropriate answers)'. This is because there may be a number of possible answers which the teacher can accept.

- '(Accept other appropriate answers)' is also used where the children's responses may use different (but correct) wording.

The conversion tables for the Progress Tests, available on the CD-ROM/digital version, provide details of the raw scores' conversion to scaled scores.

The standardisation tables for the Topic Tests, also available on the CD-ROM/digital version, provide information about comparing the raw score to the expected standard.

HeadStart
primary

Science

Year 3

Scaled Score Progress Tests

PUPIL VERSIONS

HeadStart
primary

Science

Year 3
Scaled Score Progress Test

Test A

Name: ....

Class: ....

Date: ....

Raw Score ....

Scaled Score ....

Section 1: Plants

1 **Parts of a plant**

Science
HeadStart
primary

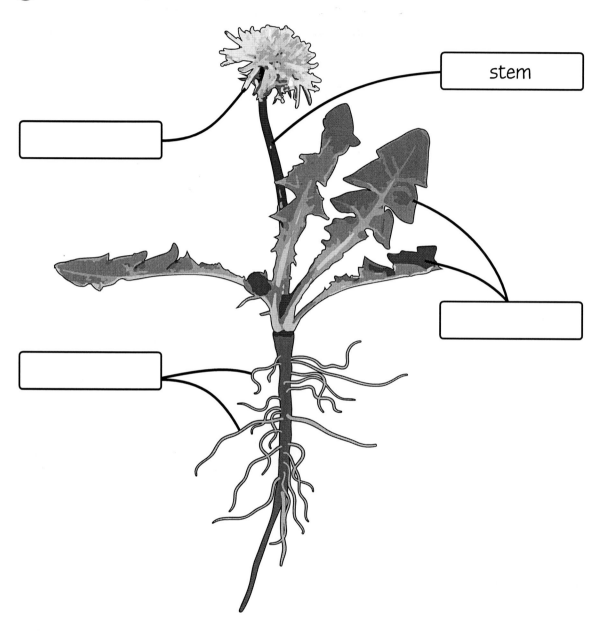

stem

Complete the following:

Write the correct part of the plant in each label.
One has been done for you.

2 marks

Page Total

Section 1: Plants

2 **Watering plants**

Science
HeadStart
primary

Draw lines to match each sentence to the correct part of the plant:

a Water evaporates from here.

stem

b They collect water from the soil.

leaves

c Moves the water through the plant to the petals and leaves.

roots

2 marks

Circle *true* or *false* next to the statements below:

d The plant gets water from the soil.

true / false

e Water collects in the flowers and passes down through the stem.

true / false

1 mark

Page Total

Section 1: Plants

3 **Plant food**

Circle *true* or *false* next to the statements below:

a The petals gather dust from the air
to feed the plant.   *true / false*

b The leaves use sunlight to create food
for the whole plant.   *true / false*

c The stem of the plant collects food from
the air.   *true / false*

2 marks

Complete the following:

d What do plants need to do to stay healthy?
Circle **one** thing.

change colour   bend in the wind   feed

1 mark

Page Total

Section 2: Animals, including humans

4 **Human skeleton**

Science
HeadStart
primary

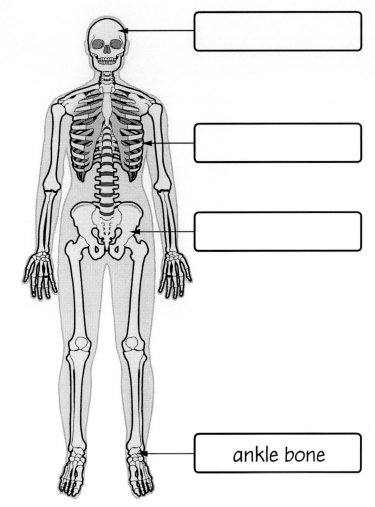

ribs
skull
pelvis
ankle bone

ankle bone

Complete the following:

a Use the words from the box above to label the bones shown in the diagram. One has been done for you.

2 marks

b Name **one** purpose of muscles in humans.

....

1 mark

Page Total

Section 2: Animals, including humans

5 **Healthy diet**

> **Circle *true* or *false* next to the statements below:**

a A good human diet will include carbohydrates, proteins and fats/oils.

true / false

b Humans can get enough water each day by eating foods such as tomatoes and melon. They don't need to drink liquid water.

true / false

1 mark

> **Complete the following:**

c Write **pasta** and **cheese** in the correct place in the table below. Two foods are already shown.

food rich in carbohydrates	food rich in fats/oils
potatoes	walnuts

1 mark

Page Total

Science
HeadStart
primary

Section 2: Animals, including humans

6 **Saturated and unsaturated fats**

saturated fats

unsaturated fats

Look at the pictures above to help you complete the following:

a Which type of fat is most necessary for a healthy, balanced diet? Circle your answer.

saturated   unsaturated

1 mark

b Which of the following contains the most unsaturated fats? Circle your answer.

biscuits   burgers   fish

1 mark

c What might happen if you eat too much unhealthy fat?

....

1 mark

Page Total

Section 3: Rocks

7 **Different kinds of rock**

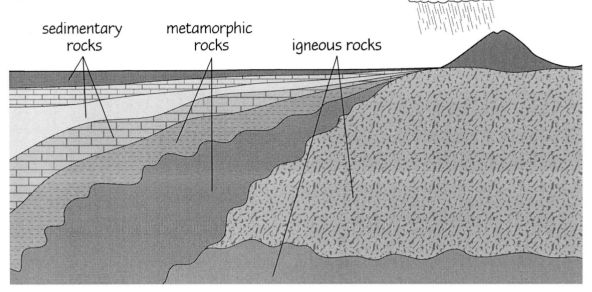

sedimentary rocks   metamorphic rocks   igneous rocks

Circle your answer to each of the following:

a Which rock is made when sedimentary or igneous rock heats up?

igneous   **sedimentary**   **metamorphic**

1 mark

b Which rock is made due to lots of heat and pressure e.g. in a volcano?

igneous   **sedimentary**   **metamorphic**

1 mark

c Man-made 'rock' can be made using material from real rock. Which of the words below is a man-made 'rock'?

igneous   **concrete**   **sedimentary**

1 mark

Page Total

Section 3: Rocks

8 **Rocks and fossils**

granite
(hard rock)

chalk
(soft rock)

marble
(hard-wearing rock)

Circle the correct words to match each of the sentences below:

a This rock is suitable for the outside of
buildings to cope with bad weather.

marble / chalk

b This rock can be used to write with.

chalk / granite

1 mark

Circle *true* or *false* next to the statements below:

c Fossils are formed only in igneous rock.

true / false

d A fossil is the preserved impression or
remains of a dead organism.

true / false

1 mark

Page Total

Section 3: Rocks

9 Soil

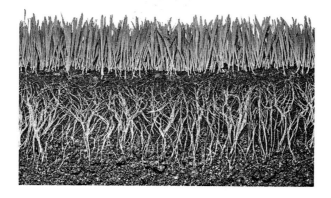

Scientists tested a sample of soil. The results were as follows:

soil is made up of	amount in soil
air	24%
water	24%
organic material	3%
minerals	49%

Answer the following questions. Use the table above to help you:

a What percentage of the soil was
made up of minerals? ....%

1 mark

b Where could the organic material have come from?
Circle your answer.

rotting plants　　　**sand**　　　**plastic bags**

1 mark

c If a type of plant grows well in well-drained soil, which soil
type would be best for them? Circle your answer.

waterproof　　**permeable**　　**impermeable**

1 mark

Page Total

Section 4: Light

10 **Light and dark**

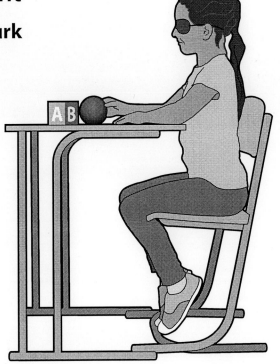

Serena is wearing a blindfold. There are objects on the table which she feels with her hands.

Circle *true* or *false* next to the statements below:

a She can tell her friends the colours of the objects. *true / false*

b She can say how many sides the objects have. *true / false*

c Serena can clearly see the objects. *true / false*

2 marks

Answer the question below:

d What is the best type of material to make a blindfold from? Circle your answer.

transparent   **opaque**   **translucent**

1 mark

Page Total

Section 4: Light

11 **Light sources**

computer screen

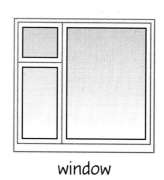

window

Sun

car headlights

Moon

Some of the objects above are light sources and some are not. Complete the table. Two have been done for you:

a

light source	not a light source
Sun	Moon

2 marks

b The Moon is not a source of light. How can it provide light on a dark night?

....

....

1 mark

Page Total

Section 4: Light

Science HeadStart primary

⑫ Sunlight

Look at the picture above and complete the following:

ⓐ Write **one** way that the people could protect their eyes from the bright sunlight.

....

1 mark

ⓑ Write **two** ways that the people could protect their skin from the bright sunlight.

1 ....

2 ....

2 marks

ⓒ Circle **one** good thing that sunlight can do for us.

age skin   provide vitamin D

keep us cool   keep us hydrated

1 mark

Page Total ◯

Section 5: Forces and magnets

13 **Magnetic material**

cobalt knife

iron nail

gold ring

aluminium can

bottle

50p coin

paperclip

pen

Write the objects pictured above in the correct place in the table below. Four have been done for you:

magnetic material	non-magnetic material
cobalt knife	gold ring
50p coin	bottle

2 marks

Page Total

Section 5: Forces and magnets

14 **Types of forces**

Complete the following:

a What is a force? Circle the best answer.

   a strong wind   **a push or pull**   **an earthquake**

○ 1 mark

b Tick **one** box to show a force which is being changed.

☐ increasing the brightness of a screen

☐ turning the sound up on a television

☐ pulling more tightly on bicycle brakes

○ 1 mark

c In a tug of war, each player is of equal strength.
Team A has 3 players and team B has 4 players.
Which team will win?

....

○ 1 mark

Page Total ○

Section 5: Forces and magnets

⓯ Friction experiment

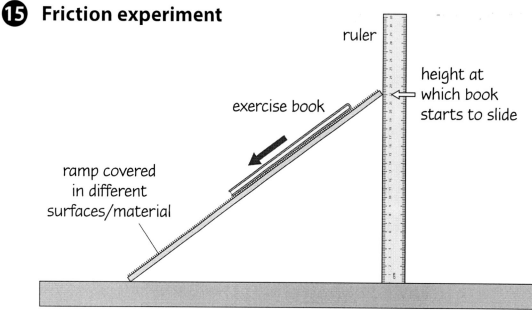

ruler

exercise book

height at which book starts to slide

ramp covered in different surfaces/material

Year 3 are testing which kind of surface creates the most friction. An exercise book is placed on a ramp, which is lifted up until the book starts to slide. The height is then marked.

The results are compared in the table below.

surface on ramp	height when book starts to slide
carpet	31 cm
wood	22 cm
sandpaper	45 cm

Complete the following:

a Which <u>surface</u> provided the greatest amount of friction?

....

1 mark

b Which <u>surface</u> provided the least friction?

....

1 mark

Page Total

Science

HeadStart
primary

Section 5: Forces and magnets

15 **Friction experiment** (continued)

c Year 3's test was a fair test. Tick **one** reason why.

☐ The same ramp surface was used each time.

☐ The same book was used each time.

☐ A different book was used each time.

1 mark

d Friction is an important force in everyday life.
Circle **two** examples of friction.

ice freezing	**hands rubbing together**
the sun shining	**a flower growing**
a car braking	**a boat floating**

2 marks

Page Total ◯   Test Total /44

HeadStart
primary

Science

Year 3
Scaled Score Progress Test

Test B

Name: ....

Class: ....

Date: ....

Raw Score ....

Scaled Score ....

Section 1: Plants

1 **Spreading out seeds**

dandelion

conker

pea pods

bird eating seeds

Complete the following:

a Circle **two** of the best ways that seeds can be spread out to places where plants can grow well.

falling in rain showers   **remaining on the plant**

carried on the fur of animals   **carried by the wind**

2 marks

Circle *true* or *false* next to the statements below:

b Birds eating seeds can help to spread the seeds.

true / false

c It is better for seeds to travel away from the parent plant.

true / false

1 mark

Page Total

Science
HeadStart
p r i m a r y

Section 1: Plants

2 **Stems**

tree trunk (stem)   pithy stem   fleshy stem

Complete the following:

a Tick **two** boxes below which describe the most important jobs of stems in plants.

☐ They carry water through the plant or tree.

☐ They are useful for putting flowers in vases.

☐ They help to keep the plant or tree upright.

☐ They are useful for small insects to climb up.

2 marks

b The flower at the top of the stem attracts bees.
Why is it important to attract bees to the flower?

....

....

1 mark

Page Total ◯

Section 1: Plants

3 **Flower head**

Circle *true* or *false* next to the statements below:

a The flower produces sweet smells to attract flying insects.

true / false

b The bright colours of the petals are attractive to insects.

true / false

c Insects land on flowers causing a lot of damage to the petals.

true / false

d The main purpose of the flower is to gather water to feed the plant.

true / false

2 marks

Page Total

Section 2: Animals, including humans

4 **Bones**

Science
HeadStart
primary

> Draw lines below to match the words to the correct pictures. One has been done for you:

a **thigh bone**

b **jaw**

c **finger bone**

d **skull**

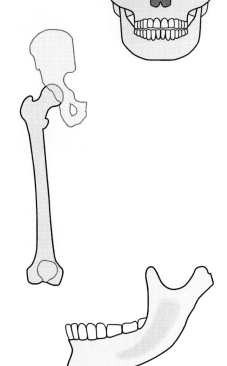

2 marks

> Complete the following:

e Bones are necessary for movement. Give another purpose for bones.

....

1 mark

Page Total

Section 2: Animals, including humans

5 **Healthy food**

 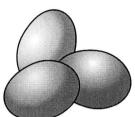  

| fruit | eggs | milk | bread |

Match the words from the box above to the descriptions below. One has been done for you:

a provides many useful vitamins and minerals .... fruit ....

b helps to keep your teeth and bones healthy ....

1 mark

c a good source of carbohydrates ....

1 mark

Circle *true* or *false* next to the statements below:

d Proteins help build and maintain muscles. *true / false*

e You can eat a healthy diet by just eating eggs and drinking milk. *true / false*

1 mark

Page Total

Section 2: Animals, including humans

6 **Types of animal skeletons**

worm

whale

crab

Circle your answer to the following:

a Which of the animals pictured above has a body with no skeleton?

worm   **whale**   **crab**

1 mark

b Some animals shed their skin several times as they grow. Which type of skeleton do these animals have?

inner skeleton   **outer skeleton**   **no skeleton**

1 mark

c Some animals have skeletons which grow with them. Which type of skeleton do these animals have?

inner skeleton   **outer skeleton**   **no skeleton**

1 mark

Page Total

Section 3: Rocks

7 **Creating soil**

Soil can be formed in different ways. **Addition** and **loss** are two of the ways in which soil forms.

> Circle the word that matches the statement below:

a Decaying vegetation increases the amount of soil.

addition / loss

1 mark

> Compost can improve the quality of the soil. Circle *true* or *false* next to the statements below:

b Compost can be formed from old newspapers and plastic containers.

true / false

c Compost can be made up of decayed plant material that has rotted over a period of time.

true / false

1 mark

Page Total

Section 3: Rocks

8 **Dinosaurs and fossils**

Velociraptor

Pterodactyl

Tyrannosaurus

Brontosaurus

Stegosaurus

| Circle *true* or *false* next to the statements below: |

a Fossils of dinosaurs help us understand the exact sounds that these extinct animals made.

true / false

b Fossils can give us a clear picture of the size of dinosaurs.

true / false

c We can tell from fossils the colour of the dinosaur's skin.

true / false

d Fossils cannot be brought back to life.

true / false

2 marks

Page Total

Science
HeadStart
p r i m a r y

Section 3: Rocks

9 **Sedimentary rock**

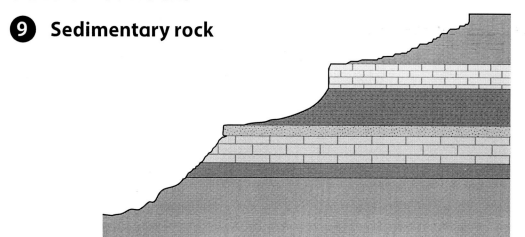

Complete the following:

a The following statements describe how sedimentary rock is created. Put them in the right order by drawing a line from the number to the correct statement. The first one has been done for you.

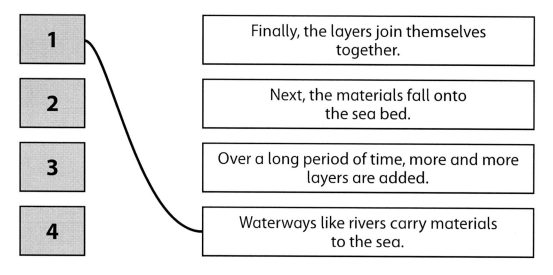

1	Finally, the layers join themselves together.
2	Next, the materials fall onto the sea bed.
3	Over a long period of time, more and more layers are added.
4	Waterways like rivers carry materials to the sea.

2 marks

b Clay can be used to make plates and bowls.
Circle **one** reason why.

It is porous.   **It can be moulded.**

It is an igneous rock.   **It is lightweight.**

1 mark

Page Total

Section 4: Light

⑩ Mirror, mirror, on the wall...

Answer the following questions:

a Bobby is looking at his reflection in the mirror. He raises his left hand. Which hand appears to be raised in the mirror?

....

1 mark

b The word below appears like this in a mirror. What is the word?

ꟼOOHƆƧ   ....

1 mark

c Circle the word '**HANDS**' as it would appear in a mirror.

ꙄꓷИАH   **SDNAH**   **HAИꓷꙄ**

1 mark

Page Total ○

Section 4: Light

Science
HeadStart
primary

11 **Light and shadow**

| Complete the following: |

a Draw the position of the shadow in the picture above.

1 mark

| Complete the following by circling the correct answer: |

b The torch is moved further away from the ball.
What happens to the shadow?

The light blocks it.   **It gets smaller.**   **It gets bigger.**

1 mark

c The ball is replaced with transparent glass.
The torch remains lit and in the same position.
What happens to the shadow?

It gets smaller.   **It disappears.**   **It gets longer.**

1 mark

Page Total

© Copyright HeadStart Primary Ltd

Section 4: Light

⑫ Letting light through

For each of the sentences below, circle the correct word to match it:

a Curtains block out light from outside.

translucent   opaque   transparent

1 mark

b What kind of material would be best to use for windows looking out into the garden?

translucent   opaque   transparent

1 mark

c What kind of material would be best to use for a blindfold?

translucent   opaque   transparent

1 mark

Page Total

Section 5: Forces and magnets

13 Magnetism

| N | ▲ | S | | S | ● | N | right → |

Look at the magnets above and complete the following:

a How could magnet ◯ be moved to the right without it being touched? Circle your answer.

Move magnet △ away from magnet ◯.

Turn magnet △ the other way.

Move magnet △ towards magnet ◯.

1 mark

b How could metal and plastic coins be separated without them being touched?

....

1 mark

Write *repel* or *attract* to complete each sentence below:

c A North Pole of a bar magnet will .... another North Pole.

d A South Pole of a bar magnet will .... a North Pole.

e A South Pole of a bar magnet will .... a South Pole.

2 marks

Page Total ◯

Section 5: Forces and magnets

14 **Faster, slower**

wood

carpet

sandpaper

Year 3 use the same amount of force to push a car along three different tracks. Each track is the same length. The children time how long it takes for the car to travel along each track.

The results are shown in the table below:

surface material	time (in seconds)
wood	2
carpet	4
sandpaper	7

Complete the following:

a What is the name of the force that slows down the car? Circle your answer.

gravity   **spring**   **friction**   **upward**

1 mark

b Which <u>surface</u> material resulted in the car travelling fastest?

....

1 mark

Page Total

Science
HeadStart
primary

Section 5: Forces and magnets

14 **Faster, slower** (continued)

c Why did the car take longer on the carpet track than on the wood track? Circle the sentence below that is correct.

The carpet is warmer so the car goes slower.

Carpet creates more friction than wood.

Wood creates more friction than carpet.

1 mark

d If the sandpaper was changed to a smoother sandpaper, how long do you think the car would take?
Circle your answer.

7 seconds   **5 seconds**   **20 seconds**

1 mark

wood

carpet

sandpaper

Page Total

Section 5: Forces and magnets

15 **Bicycle**

brake handle

pedals

Charlotte wants to ride her bike above along a flat road.

Complete the following:

a What force could Charlotte use on the pedals to make the bicycle travel forwards? Circle your answer.

pull **push** **twist**

1 mark

b What should Charlotte do to the brake handle to make the bicycle slow down?

. . . .

1 mark

c As Charlotte is slowing down, a dog runs out in front of her. Explain how Charlotte could stop as quickly as possible.

. . . .

1 mark

Page Total

Test Total /44

HeadStart
primary

Science

Year 3
Scaled Score Progress Test

Test C

Name: ....

Class: ....

Date: ....

Raw Score ....

Scaled Score ....

Section 1: Plants

1 **Growing plants**

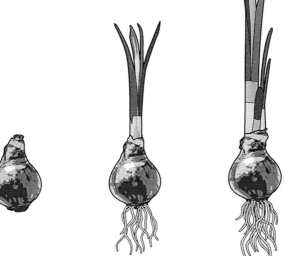

Circle your answers to the following:

a Which **two** of the things below are most important for the growth of plants?

sunlight   wind   water   birds

2 marks

b Why does a plant need leaves to help it grow?
Circle the best answer.

They take water   They make food   They attract
from the soil.   from sunlight.   birds.

1 mark

Page Total

Section 1: Plants

2 **Plant experiment**

white
flower

Science

HeadStart
p r i m a r y

stem

A white flower is cut
at the stem and placed in
a glass vase of water which
has blue food colouring added.

water with
blue food
colouring
added

glass vase

Answer the following questions:

a What will happen to the white petals of the flower over time?

....

1 mark

b Why does this happen?

....

....

1 mark

Circle *true* or *false* next to the statements below:

c Roots have tiny hairs which gather water
from the soil.

true / false

d Water is collected by the flower and
moved down through the stem.

true / false

1 mark

Page Total

Section 1: Plants

3 **Functions of parts of flowering plants**

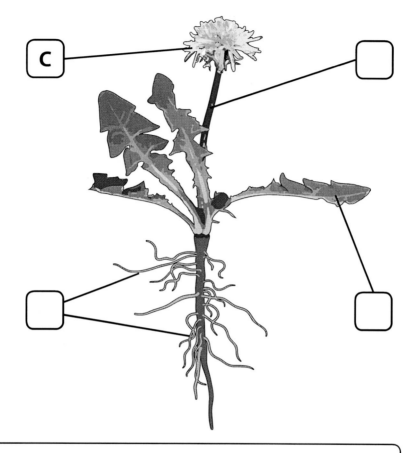

Look at the picture above to complete the following:

a Label the flowering plant **A**, **B**, **C** or **D** to match the statements below. One has been done for you.

A: They gather water to feed the plant.

B: Water evaporates from them.

C: Their colours are attractive to insects.

D: It helps to keep the plant upright.

2 marks

b Which part of the plant also produces sweet smells?

....

1 mark

Page Total

Section 2: Animals, including humans

4 **Human skeleton**

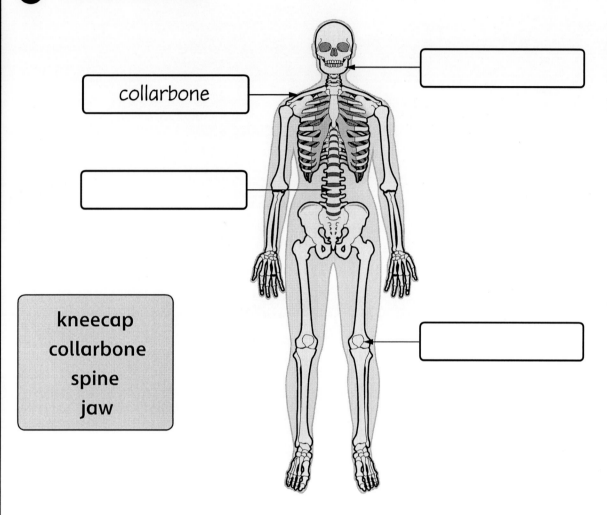

collarbone

kneecap
collarbone
spine
jaw

Complete the following:

a Use the words from the box above to label the bones in the diagram. One has been done for you.

2 marks

b Why do humans have a rib cage?

....

1 mark

Page Total

Section 2: Animals, including humans

5 **Vertebrates and invertebrates**

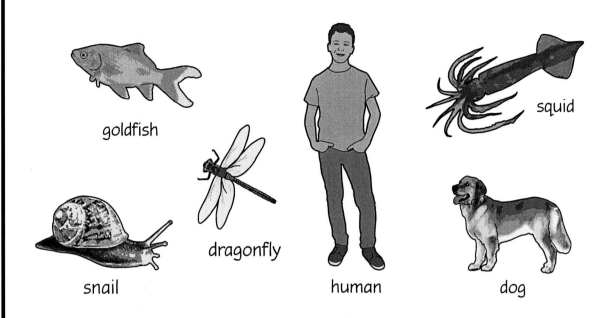

goldfish

squid

dragonfly

snail

human

dog

Look at the pictures of some vertebrates and invertebrates to help you complete the following:

a Animals with no backbone are called ....

1 mark

b Three of the living things pictured above are vertebrates. Write them in the table. One has been done for you.

vertebrates
human

2 marks

Page Total

Section 2: Animals, including humans

Science
HeadStart
p r i m a r y

6 **Healthy diet**

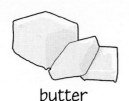
butter

apple

chips

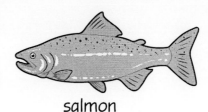
salmon

Complete the questions below:

a Which of the foods above is a fruit?

. . . .

1 mark

b Which of the foods above contains the highest amount of protein?

. . . .

1 mark

c Which of the foods above is usually made from dairy?

. . . .

1 mark

d Chips are a source of carbohydrates.
Write one reason why we need some carbohydrates in our diet.

. . . .

1 mark

Page Total

Section 3: Rocks

7 **Soil**

Complete the following:

a About a quarter of soil is made up of water.
Circle **one** way that water gets into the soil.

from birds   **from rain falling**   **from flowers**

1 mark

b A small amount of soil is made up of organic material.
Circle **one** way that organic material naturally gets into soil.

from plastic   **from rotting plants**   **from gravel**

1 mark

c A gardener needs well-drained soil for tomato plants to grow.
Which kind of soil would be most suitable?
Circle your answer.

permeable   **impermeable**   **waterproof**

1 mark

Page Total

Section 3: Rocks

8 **Types of rock**

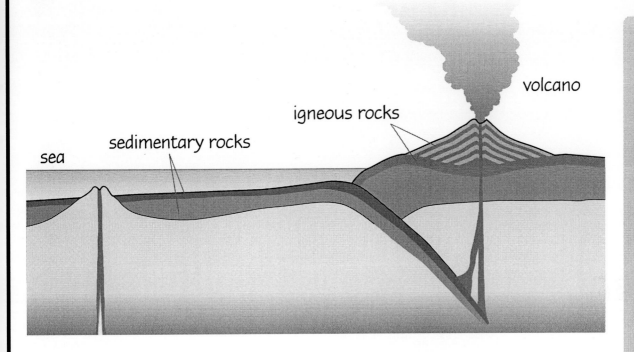

sea

sedimentary rocks

igneous rocks

volcano

Circle *true* or *false* next to the statements below:

a Igneous rock is made from layers of minerals that have settled on the sea bed over time.

true / false

b Building bricks made from clay are very permeable.

true / false

c Fossils are only formed in sedimentary rock.

true / false

d Permeable rock is suitable for the outside of buildings.

true / false

2 marks

Page Total

Section 3: Rocks

9 **Fossils**

trace fossil – a footprint

body fossil – formed from the
remains of a dead animal or plant

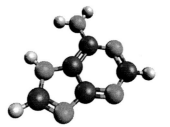

chemical fossil – chemicals
found in rocks

Circle the correct words to match the statements below:

a This kind of fossil is formed from the
remains of a dead animal or plant.

trace / body

b Ancient footsteps found at low tide are
an example of this kind of fossil.

chemical / trace

c You can't see this fossil but it can
be found in rocks.

chemical / body

2 marks

Circle *true* or *false* next to the statements below:

d It is very unlikely that fossils are found
in igneous rock.

true / false

e Fossils can be found in rock which
formed 500 years ago.

true / false

1 mark

Page Total

Section 4: Light

⑩ Shadows

Matthias shines a torch at a clown puppet. The shadow of the puppet is seen on the wall.

| Circle the correct answer to each of the following: |

a What kind of material would not form a shadow?

translucent **opaque** **transparent**

1 mark

b What kind of material is the clown?

translucent **opaque** **transparent**

1 mark

c When the torch moves away from the puppet, what happens to the size of the shadow? Circle your answer.

It gets smaller. **It gets bigger.** **It stays the same.**

1 mark

d When the torch moves to the left of the puppet, what happens to the shadow? Circle your answer.

It moves left. **It moves right.** **It stays still.**

1 mark

Page Total ◯

Section 4: Light

⑪ Harmful or helpful sunshine?

can cause skin cancer	can provide warmth
provides us with Vitamin D	
helps plants make food	causes skin to wrinkle

Complete the following:

a The Sun can be good for you and bad for you at the same time. Put the things in the box above into the correct place in the table below. Two have been done for you.

helpful (good)	harmful (bad)
provides us with vitamin D	can cause skin cancer

2 marks

b Explain how you can keep your skin safe from the Sun when playing outdoors during summer months.

....

1 mark

Page Total

Section 4: Light

12 **Sources of light**

Moon

Sun

window

lamp

mirror

Complete the following:

a Which **two** of the items above are sources of light?

1 ....

2 ....

2 marks

Circle *true* or *false* next to the statements below:

If you need to create complete darkness in a room you only need to:

b Remove all sources of light.   *true / false*

c Wear sunglasses.   *true / false*

1 mark

Page Total

Section 5: Forces and magnets

13 **Everyday magnets**

S		N

Complete the following:

a How could a magnet be used to sort items in a recycling centre?

....

....

1 mark

b Suffaya has a magnetic picture frame. Which of the following objects will it **not** be attracted to?
Circle your answer.

fridge   **wallpaper**   **radiator**

1 mark

Write *attract* or *repel* next to each pair of magnets below:

c | S | N | | N | S | ....

d | N | S | | N | S | ....

1 mark

Page Total

Section 5: Forces and magnets

14 **Magnet strength**

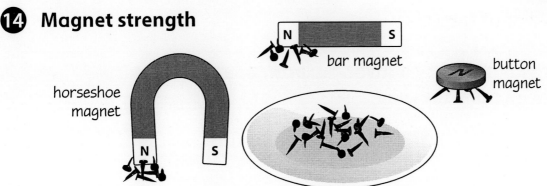

horseshoe magnet

bar magnet

button magnet

Year 3A carried out an experiment to see how strong three magnets are. The results are shown in the table below.

magnet	number of iron tacks picked up
button magnet	4
horseshoe magnet	10
bar magnet	7

Answer the following questions:

a Which magnet was the strongest? .... 1 mark

3B were also testing the strength of different magnets. In their experiment, the horseshoe magnet picked up paper clips, the button magnet picked up drawing pins and the bar magnet picked up iron nails.

b 3B's test was not a fair test. Circle the sentence below which explains why not.

They used different magnets.

Drawing pins aren't magnetic.

1 mark

Each magnet picked up a different thing.

Page Total

Section 5: Forces and magnets

15 **Which kind of force?**

Circle which kind of force is involved; *push* or *pull*.
Two have been done for you:

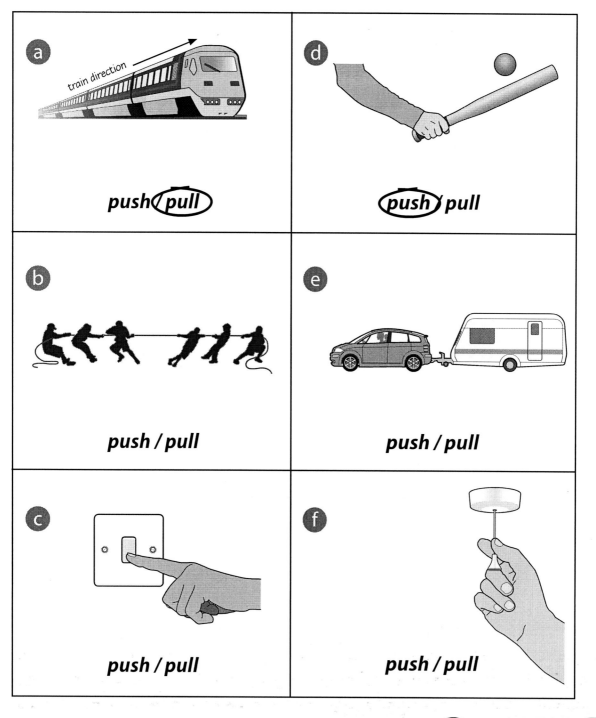

a *push /* ~~pull~~ (circled)

d ~~push~~ (circled) *pull*

b *push / pull*

e *push / pull*

c *push / pull*

f *push / pull*

2 marks

Page Total ◯

Test Total /44

HeadStart
primary

Science

Year 3

Scaled Score Progress Tests

ANSWER VERSIONS

HeadStart
primary

Science

Year 3
Scaled Score Progress Test

Test A

ANSWERS

Section 1: Plants

Parts of a plant

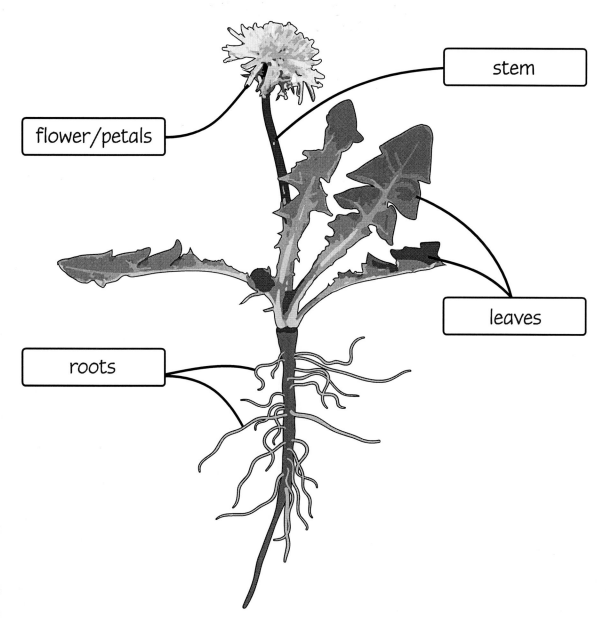

flower/petals

stem

leaves

roots

Complete the following:

Write the correct part of the plant in each label.
One has been done for you.

(2 marks for all 3 correct, 1 mark for 2 correct.)

2

2 marks

Page Total **2**

Science
HeadStart
p r i m a r y

Section 1: Plants

2 Watering plants

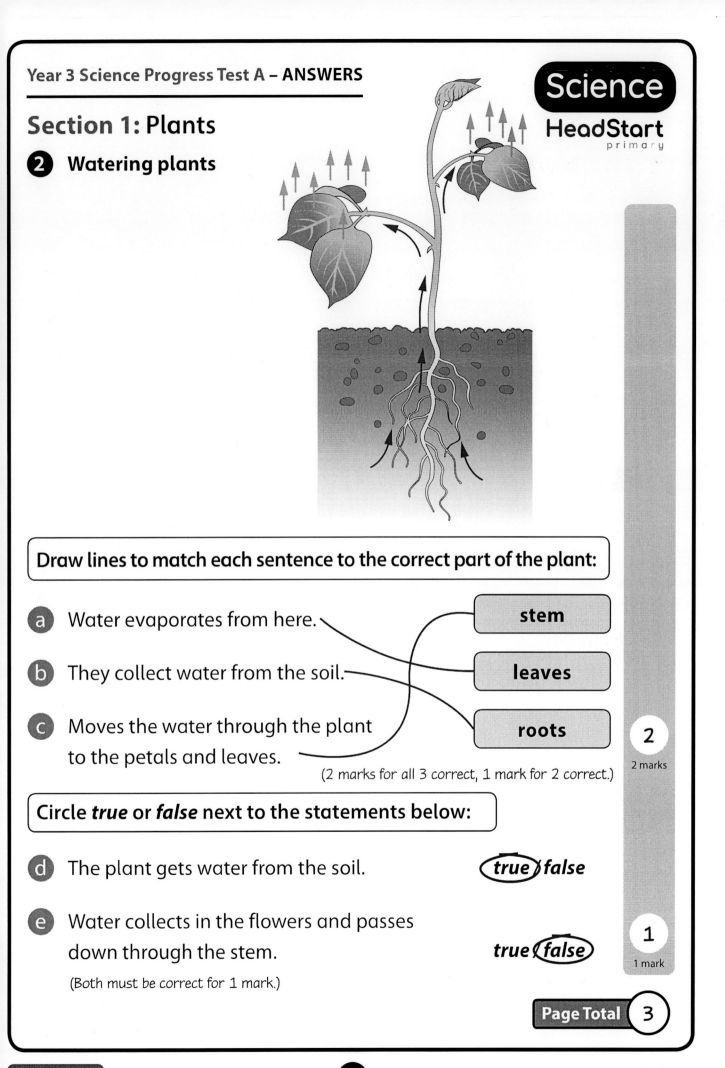

Science
HeadStart
primary

Draw lines to match each sentence to the correct part of the plant:

a Water evaporates from here.

b They collect water from the soil.

c Moves the water through the plant to the petals and leaves.

stem

leaves

roots

(2 marks for all 3 correct, 1 mark for 2 correct.)

2

2 marks

Circle *true* or *false* next to the statements below:

d The plant gets water from the soil.

true false

e Water collects in the flowers and passes down through the stem.

true **false**

(Both must be correct for 1 mark.)

1

1 mark

Page Total **3**

Section 1: Plants

3 **Plant food**

Science
HeadStart
primary

Circle *true* or *false* next to the statements below:

a The petals gather dust from the air to feed the plant.

true **false**

b The leaves use sunlight to create food for the whole plant.

true false

c The stem of the plant collects food from the air.

true **false**

2

2 marks

(2 marks for all 3 correct, 1 mark for 2 correct.)

Complete the following:

d What do plants need to do to stay healthy? Circle **one** thing.

change colour   **bend in the wind**   feed

1

1 mark

Page Total **3**

Science
HeadStart
primary

Section 2: Animals, including humans

4 **Human skeleton**

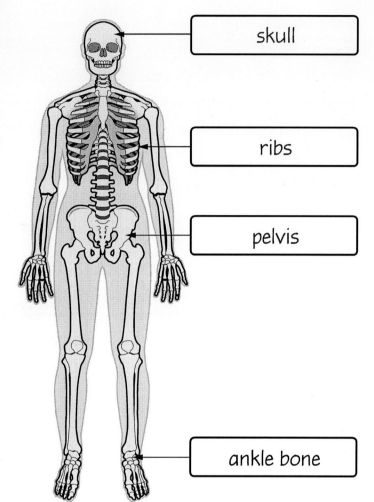

skull

ribs

pelvis

ankle bone

ribs
skull
pelvis
ankle bone

Complete the following:

a Use the words from the box above to label the bones shown in the diagram. One has been done for you.

(2 marks for all 3 correct, 1 mark for 2 correct.)

2

2 marks

b Name **one** purpose of muscles in humans.

Answer should suggest they help movement / support the skeleton.

1

1 mark

Page Total **3**

Section 2: Animals, including humans

Science
HeadStart
primary

5 **Healthy diet**

Circle *true* or *false* next to the statements below:

a A good human diet will include carbohydrates, proteins and fats/oils.

true /false

b Humans can get enough water each day by eating foods such as tomatoes and melon. They don't need to drink liquid water.

true /false

1
1 mark

(Both must be correct for 1 mark.)

Complete the following:

c Write **pasta** and **cheese** in the correct place in the table below. Two foods are already shown.

food rich in carbohydrates	food rich in fats/oils
potatoes	walnuts
pasta	cheese

(Both must be correct for 1 mark.)

1
1 mark

Page Total **2**

Section 2: Animals, including humans

6 **Saturated and unsaturated fats**

saturated fats

unsaturated fats

Look at the pictures above to help you complete the following:

a Which type of fat is most necessary for a healthy, balanced diet? Circle your answer.

saturated   **(unsaturated)**

1

1 mark

b Which of the following contains the most unsaturated fats? Circle your answer.

biscuits   **burgers**   **(fish)**

1

1 mark

c What might happen if you eat too much unhealthy fat?

Answer should suggest an appropriate detriment to health.

1

1 mark

Page Total 3

Science
HeadStart
primary

Section 3: Rocks

7 **Different kinds of rock**

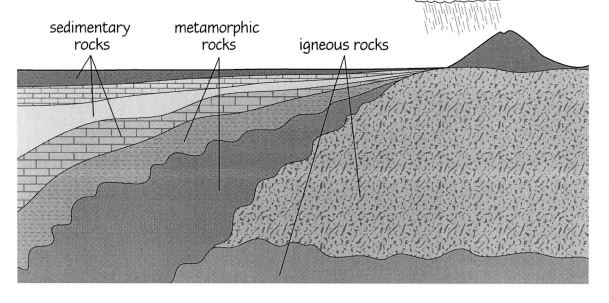

sedimentary rocks   metamorphic rocks   igneous rocks

Circle your answer to each of the following:

a Which rock is made when sedimentary or igneous rock heats up?

    igneous   sedimentary   (metamorphic)

1
1 mark

b Which rock is made due to lots of heat and pressure e.g. in a volcano?

    (igneous)   sedimentary   metamorphic

1
1 mark

c Man-made 'rock' can be made using material from real rock. Which of the words below is a man-made 'rock'?

    igneous   (concrete)   sedimentary

1
1 mark

Page Total **3**

Section 3: Rocks

8 **Rocks and fossils**

granite
(hard rock)

chalk
(soft rock)

marble
(hard-wearing rock)

Circle the correct words to match each of the sentences below:

a This rock is suitable for the outside of buildings to cope with bad weather.

b This rock can be used to write with.

(Both must be correct for 1 mark.)

1
1 mark

Circle _true_ or _false_ next to the statements below:

c Fossils are formed only in igneous rock.

d A fossil is the preserved impression or remains of a dead organism.

(Both must be correct for 1 mark.)

1
1 mark

Page Total **2**

Section 3: Rocks

9 **Soil**

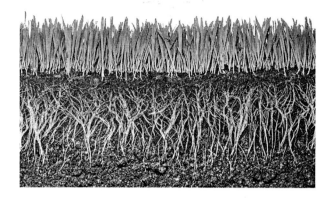

Scientists tested a sample of soil. The results were as follows:

soil is made up of	amount in soil
air	24%
water	24%
organic material	3%
minerals	49%

Answer the following questions. Use the table above to help you:

a What percentage of the soil was made up of minerals? ....49............%

1
1 mark

b Where could the organic material have come from? Circle your answer.

(rotting plants)   sand   plastic bags

1
1 mark

c If a type of plant grows well in well-drained soil, which soil type would be best for them? Circle your answer.

waterproof   (permeable)   impermeable

1
1 mark

Page Total **3**

Section 4: Light

⑩ Light and dark

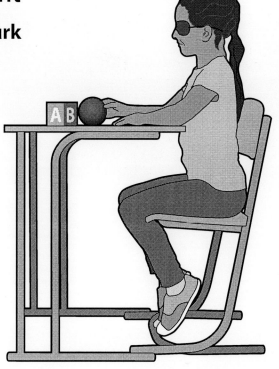

Serena is wearing a blindfold. There are objects on the table which she feels with her hands.

Circle *true* or *false* next to the statements below:

a She can tell her friends the colours of the objects.   *true* ~~*false*~~

b She can say how many sides the objects have.   *true* *false*

c Serena can clearly see the objects.   *true* *false*

(2 marks for all 3 correct, 1 mark for 2 correct.)

2

2 marks

Answer the question below:

d What is the best type of material to make a blindfold from? Circle your answer.

transparent   **opaque**   **translucent**

1

1 mark

Page Total **3**

Science
HeadStart
primary

Section 4: Light

⑪ Light sources

computer screen

window

Sun

car headlights

Moon

Some of the objects above are light sources and some are not.
Complete the table. Two have been done for you:

ⓐ

light source	not a light source
Sun	Moon
car headlights	window
computer screen	

(2 marks for all 3 correct, 1 mark for 2 correct.)

2

2 marks

ⓑ The Moon is not a source of light. How can it provide light on a dark night?

Answer should suggest it reflects light from the Sun.

1

1 mark

Page Total **3**

Section 4: Light

12 Sunlight

Look at the picture above and complete the following:

a Write **one** way that the people could protect their eyes from the bright sunlight.

Answer should suggest protection of eyes e.g. wearing sunglasses / peaked cap.

1
1 mark

b Write **two** ways that the people could protect their skin from the bright sunlight.

1 Answers should suggest protection of skin

2 e.g. suncream / clothing / shade

2
2 marks

c Circle **one** good thing that sunlight can do for us.

age skin   (provide vitamin D)

keep us cool   keep us hydrated

1
1 mark

Page Total **4**

Science
HeadStart
primary

Section 5: Forces and magnets

⑬ **Magnetic material**

cobalt knife

iron nail

gold ring

aluminium can

bottle

50p coin

pen

paperclip

Write the objects pictured above in the correct place in the table below. Four have been done for you:

magnetic material	non-magnetic material
cobalt knife	gold ring
50p coin	bottle
paper clip	pen
iron nail	aluminium can

2

2 marks

(2 marks for all 4 correct, 1 mark for 3 correct.)

Page Total ②

Section 5: Forces and magnets

14 **Types of forces**

Complete the following:

a What is a force? Circle the best answer.

a strong wind   (a push or pull)   an earthquake

1
1 mark

b Tick **one** box to show a force which is being changed.

☐ increasing the brightness of a screen

☐ turning the sound up on a television

☑ pulling more tightly on bicycle brakes

1
1 mark

c In a tug of war, each player is of equal strength.
Team A has 3 players and team B has 4 players.
Which team will win?

Team B

1
1 mark

Page Total **3**

Section 5: Forces and magnets

15 **Friction experiment**

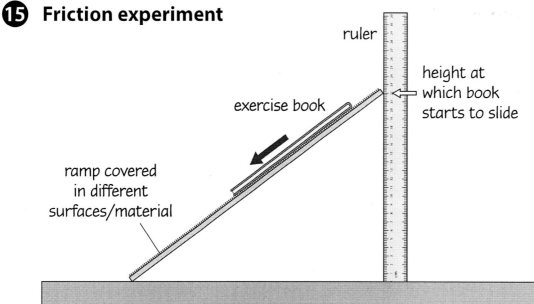

ruler

height at which book starts to slide

exercise book

ramp covered in different surfaces/material

Year 3 are testing which kind of surface creates the most friction. An exercise book is placed on a ramp, which is lifted up until the book starts to slide. The height is then marked.

The results are compared in the table below.

surface on ramp	height when book starts to slide
carpet	31 cm
wood	22 cm
sandpaper	45 cm

Complete the following:

a Which <u>surface</u> provided the greatest amount of friction?

.... sandpaper ....

1

1 mark

b Which <u>surface</u> provided the least friction?

.... wood ....

1

1 mark

Page Total 2

Section 5: Forces and magnets

15 **Friction experiment** (continued)

Science
HeadStart
primary

c Year 3's test was a fair test. Tick **one** reason why.

☐ The same ramp surface was used each time.

☑ The same book was used each time.

☐ A different book was used each time.

1
1 mark

d Friction is an important force in everyday life.
Circle **two** examples of friction.

ice freezing   （hands rubbing together）

the sun shining   a flower growing

（a car braking）   a boat floating

2
2 marks

Page Total **3**   Test Total **44 /44**

HeadStart
primary

Science

Year 3
Scaled Score Progress Test

Test B

ANSWERS

Section 1: Plants

1 **Spreading out seeds**

dandelion

conker

pea pods

bird eating seeds

Complete the following:

a Circle **two** of the best ways that seeds can be spread out to places where plants can grow well.

falling in rain showers   **remaining on the plant**

carried on the fur of animals

carried by the wind

2

2 marks

Circle _true_ or _false_ next to the statements below:

b Birds eating seeds can help to spread the seeds.

true false

c It is better for seeds to travel away from the parent plant.

true false

1

1 mark

(Both must be correct for 1 mark.)

Page Total **3**

Section 1: Plants

2 **Stems**

tree trunk (stem)

pithy stem

fleshy stem

Complete the following:

a Tick **two** boxes below which describe the most important jobs of stems in plants.

[✓] They carry water through the plant or tree.

[ ] They are useful for putting flowers in vases.

[✓] They help to keep the plant or tree upright.

[ ] They are useful for small insects to climb up.

2

2 marks

b The flower at the top of the stem attracts bees.
Why is it important to attract bees to the flower?

Answer should suggest bees collect pollen or nectar.
....

....

1

1 mark

Page Total **3**

Section 1: Plants

3 Flower head

Circle *true* or *false* next to the statements below:

a The flower produces sweet smells to attract flying insects.

~~true~~ false

b The bright colours of the petals are attractive to insects.

~~true~~ false

c Insects land on flowers causing a lot of damage to the petals.

true ~~false~~

d The main purpose of the flower is to gather water to feed the plant.

true ~~false~~

(2 marks for all 4 correct, 1 mark for 3 correct.)

2

2 marks

Page Total **2**

Section 2: Animals, including humans

4 **Bones**

> Draw lines below to match the words to the correct pictures. One has been done for you:

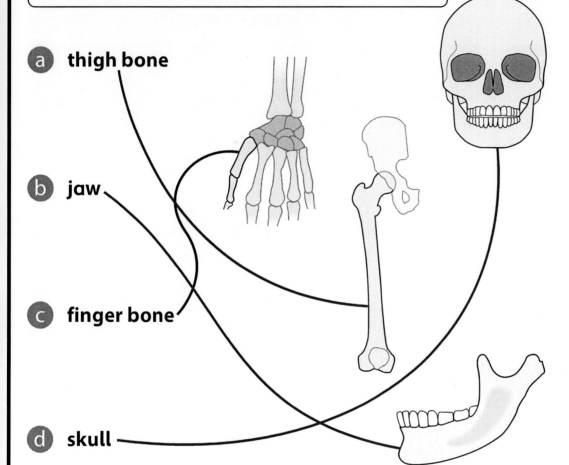

a **thigh bone**

b **jaw**

c **finger bone**

d **skull**

(2 marks for all 3 correct, 1 mark for 2 correct.)

2
2 marks

> Complete the following:

e Bones are necessary for movement. Give another purpose for bones.
Answer should suggest they support the body / protect organs / allow movement.

1
1 mark

Page Total **3**

Section 2: Animals, including humans

Science
HeadStart
primary

5 **Healthy food**

 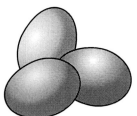  

| fruit | eggs | milk | bread |

Match the words from the box above to the descriptions below. One has been done for you:

a provides many useful vitamins and minerals .... fruit

b helps to keep your teeth and bones healthy .... milk **1** 1 mark

c a good source of carbohydrates .... bread **1** 1 mark

Circle *true* or *false* next to the statements below:

d Proteins help build and maintain muscles. **true** false

e You can eat a healthy diet by just eating eggs and drinking milk. true **false** **1** 1 mark

(Both must be correct for 1 mark.)

Page Total **3**

Section 3: Rocks

8 **Dinosaurs and fossils**

Velociraptor

Pterodactyl

Tyrannosaurus

Brontosaurus

Stegosaurus

Circle *true* or *false* next to the statements below:

a Fossils of dinosaurs help us understand the exact sounds that these extinct animals made.

 true (false)

b Fossils can give us a clear picture of the size of dinosaurs.

 (true) false

c We can tell from fossils the colour of the dinosaur's skin.

 true (false)

d Fossils cannot be brought back to life.

 (true) false

(2 marks for all 4 correct, 1 mark for 3 correct.)

2

2 marks

Page Total **2**

Section 3: Rocks

9 **Sedimentary rock**

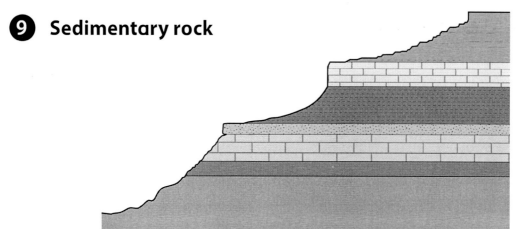

Science

HeadStart
primary

Complete the following:

a The following statements describe how sedimentary rock is created. Put them in the right order by drawing a line from the number to the correct statement. The first one has been done for you.

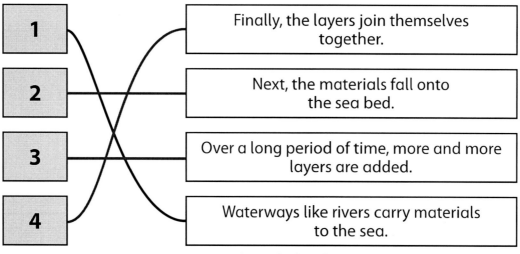

1	Finally, the layers join themselves together.
2	Next, the materials fall onto the sea bed.
3	Over a long period of time, more and more layers are added.
4	Waterways like rivers carry materials to the sea.

(2 marks for all 3 correct, 1 mark for 2 correct.)

b Clay can be used to make plates and bowls.
Circle **one** reason why.

It is porous.   (It can be moulded.)

It is an igneous rock.   It is lightweight.

2

2 marks

1

1 mark

Page Total **3**

Section 4: Light

Science
HeadStart
primary

⑩ Mirror, mirror, on the wall…

| Answer the following questions: |

a Bobby is looking at his reflection in the mirror. He raises his left hand. Which hand appears to be raised in the mirror?

.... right hand ....

1
1 mark

b The word below appears like this in a mirror. What is the word?

SCHOOL (mirrored)   SCHOOL
....

1
1 mark

c Circle the word '**HANDS**' as it would appear in a mirror.

HANDS (mirrored, circled)   SDNAH   HANDS (reversed)

1
1 mark

Page Total **3**

Section 4: Light

11 **Light and shadow**

shadow drawn in an appropriate position

| Complete the following: |

a Draw the position of the shadow in the picture above.
Accept an appropriate position of the shadow.

1
1 mark

| Complete the following by circling the correct answer: |

b The torch is moved further away from the ball.
What happens to the shadow?

The light blocks it.   (**It gets smaller.**)   **It gets bigger.**

1
1 mark

c The ball is replaced with transparent glass.
The torch remains lit and in the same position.
What happens to the shadow?

It gets smaller.   (**It disappears.**)   **It gets longer.**

1
1 mark

Page Total **3**

Section 4: Light

Science
HeadStart
primary

12 **Letting light through**

For each of the sentences below, circle the correct word to match it:

a Curtains block out light from outside.

translucent   **(opaque)**   transparent

1
1 mark

b What kind of material would be best to use for windows looking out into the garden?

translucent   opaque   **(transparent)**

1
1 mark

c What kind of material would be best to use for a blindfold?

translucent   **(opaque)**   transparent

1
1 mark

Page Total **3**

Section 5: Forces and magnets

Science
HeadStart
primary

13 **Magnetism**

N ▲ S   S ● N   right →

Look at the magnets above and complete the following:

a How could magnet ◯ be moved to the right without it being touched? Circle your answer.

Move magnet △ away from magnet ◯.

Turn magnet △ the other way.

Move magnet △ towards magnet ◯.

1
1 mark

b How could metal and plastic coins be separated without them being touched?

Use a magnet.

1
1 mark

Write *repel* or *attract* to complete each sentence below:

c A North Pole of a bar magnet will ……*repel*…… another North Pole.

d A South Pole of a bar magnet will ……*attract*…… a North Pole.

e A South Pole of a bar magnet will ……*repel*…… a South Pole.

2
2 marks

(2 marks for all 3 correct, 1 mark for 2 correct.)

Page Total **4**

Science
HeadStart
primary

Section 2: Animals, including humans

6 Types of animal skeletons

worm

whale

crab

Circle your answer to the following:

a Which of the animals pictured above has a body with no skeleton?

worm   **whale**   **crab**

1

1 mark

b Some animals shed their skin several times as they grow. Which type of skeleton do these animals have?

inner skeleton    **outer skeleton**   **no skeleton**

1

1 mark

c Some animals have skeletons which grow with them. Which type of skeleton do these animals have?

inner skeleton   **outer skeleton**   **no skeleton**

1

1 mark

Page Total **3**

Section 3: Rocks

7 **Creating soil**

Soil can be formed in different ways. **Addition** and **loss** are two of the ways in which soil forms.

Circle the word that matches the statement below:

a Decaying vegetation increases the amount of soil.

~~addition~~ / loss

1

1 mark

Compost can improve the quality of the soil.
Circle *true* or *false* next to the statements below:

b Compost can be formed from old newspapers and plastic containers.

true (false)

c Compost can be made up of decayed plant material that has rotted over a period of time.

(true) false

1

1 mark

(Both must be correct for 1 mark.)

Page Total 2

Section 5: Forces and magnets

14 **Faster, slower**

wood

carpet

sandpaper

Year 3 use the same amount of force to push a car along three different tracks. Each track is the same length. The children time how long it takes for the car to travel along each track.

The results are shown in the table below:

surface material	time (in seconds)
wood	2
carpet	4
sandpaper	7

Complete the following:

a What is the name of the force that slows down the car? Circle your answer.

    gravity   **spring**   **(friction)**   **upward**

1
1 mark

b Which <u>surface</u> material resulted in the car travelling fastest?

 wood

1
1 mark

Page Total **2**

Section 5: Forces and magnets

14 **Faster, slower** (continued)

c Why did the car take longer on the carpet track than on the wood track? Circle the sentence below that is correct.

The carpet is warmer so the car goes slower.

Carpet creates more friction than wood.

Wood creates more friction than carpet.

1
1 mark

d If the sandpaper was changed to a smoother sandpaper, how long do you think the car would take?
Circle your answer.

7 seconds   **5 seconds**   **20 seconds**

1
1 mark

wood

carpet

sandpaper

Page Total **2**

Section 5: Forces and magnets

15 Bicycle

brake handle

pedals

Charlotte wants to ride her bike above along a flat road.

Complete the following:

a What force could Charlotte use on the pedals to make the bicycle travel forwards? Circle your answer.

    pull   **push**   **twist**

1

1 mark

b What should Charlotte do to the brake handle to make the bicycle slow down?

Answer should indicate pulling the handle.

1

1 mark

c As Charlotte is slowing down, a dog runs out in front of her. Explain how Charlotte could stop as quickly as possible.

Answer should suggest increasing the friction
e.g. pulling brake harder / putting feet down

1

1 mark

Page Total **3**

Test Total **44 /44**

HeadStart
primary

Science

Year 3
Scaled Score Progress Test

Test C

ANSWERS

Section 1: Plants

1 **Growing plants**

Circle your answers to the following:

a Which **two** of the things below are most important for the growth of plants?

 sunlight   wind   water   birds

 2
2 marks

b Why does a plant need leaves to help it grow?
Circle the best answer.

They take water from the soil.   They make food from sunlight.   They attract birds.

1
1 mark

Page Total 3

Section 1: Plants

2 **Plant experiment**

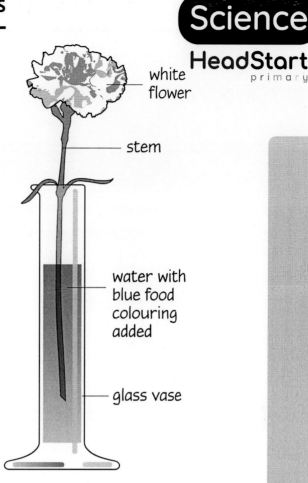

white flower

stem

water with blue food colouring added

glass vase

A white flower is cut at the stem and placed in a glass vase of water which has blue food colouring added.

Answer the following questions:

a What will happen to the white petals of the flower over time?
They will turn blue.

1
1 mark

b Why does this happen?
Answer should suggest water travelling up the stem.

1
1 mark

Circle *true* or *false* next to the statements below:

c Roots have tiny hairs which gather water from the soil.

true false

d Water is collected by the flower and moved down through the stem.

true **false**

(Both must be correct for 1 mark.)

1
1 mark

Page Total **3**

Section 1: Plants

3 **Functions of parts of flowering plants**

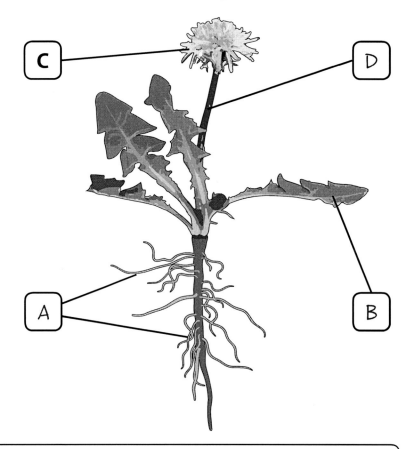

Look at the picture above to complete the following:

a Label the flowering plant **A**, **B**, **C** or **D** to match the statements below. One has been done for you.

A: They gather water to feed the plant.

B: Water evaporates from them.

C: Their colours are attractive to insects.

D: It helps to keep the plant upright.

(2 marks for all 3 correct, 1 mark for 2 correct.)

2

2 marks

b Which part of the plant also produces sweet smells?

flower/petals

1

1 mark

Page Total **3**

Section 2: Animals, including humans

4 Human skeleton

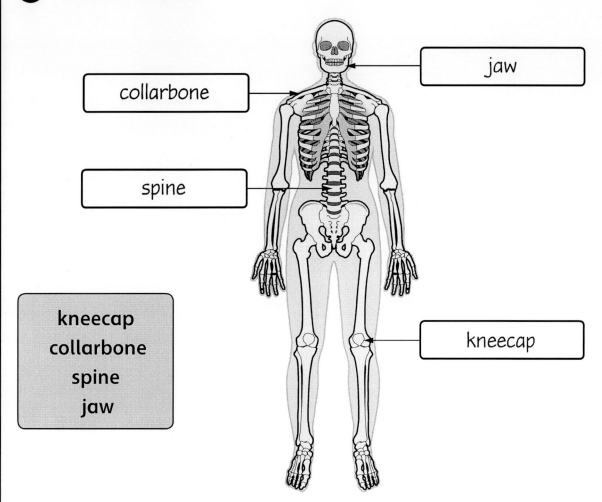

collarbone

jaw

spine

kneecap

kneecap
collarbone
spine
jaw

Complete the following:

a Use the words from the box above to label the bones in the diagram. One has been done for you.

(2 marks for all 3 correct, 1 mark for 2 correct.)

2

2 marks

b Why do humans have a rib cage?

Answer should suggest to protect the internal organs /
help respiration / help support chest and back

(Accept other appropriate answers.)

1

1 mark

Page Total **3**

Science
HeadStart
p r i m a r y

Section 2: Animals, including humans

5 **Vertebrates and invertebrates**

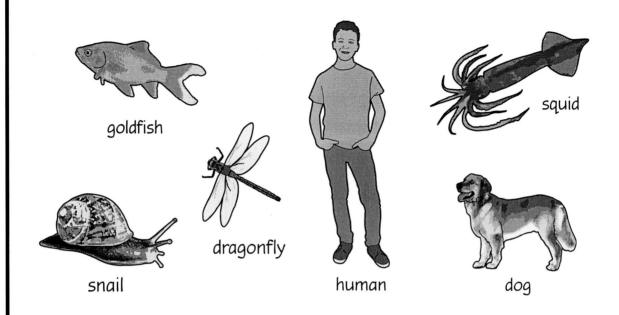

goldfish

squid

snail

dragonfly

human

dog

Look at the pictures of some vertebrates and invertebrates to help you complete the following:

a Animals with no backbone are called .... invertebrates ....

1

1 mark

b Three of the living things pictured above are vertebrates. Write them in the table. One has been done for you.

vertebrates
human
goldfish
dog

2

2 marks

Page Total **3**

Section 2: Animals, including humans

Science
HeadStart
primary

6 **Healthy diet**

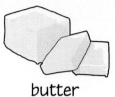
butter

apple

chips

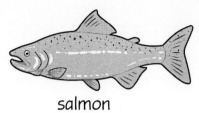
salmon

Complete the questions below:

a Which of the foods above is a fruit?

apple
....

1
1 mark

b Which of the foods above contains the highest amount
of protein?

salmon
....

1
1 mark

c Which of the foods above is usually made from dairy?

butter
....

1
1 mark

d Chips are a source of carbohydrates.
Write one reason why we need some carbohydrates in
our diet.

Answer should suggest they provide energy / help build
....
muscle / help digestion.

1
1 mark

Page Total **4**

Section 3: Rocks

7 Soil

Science
HeadStart
primary

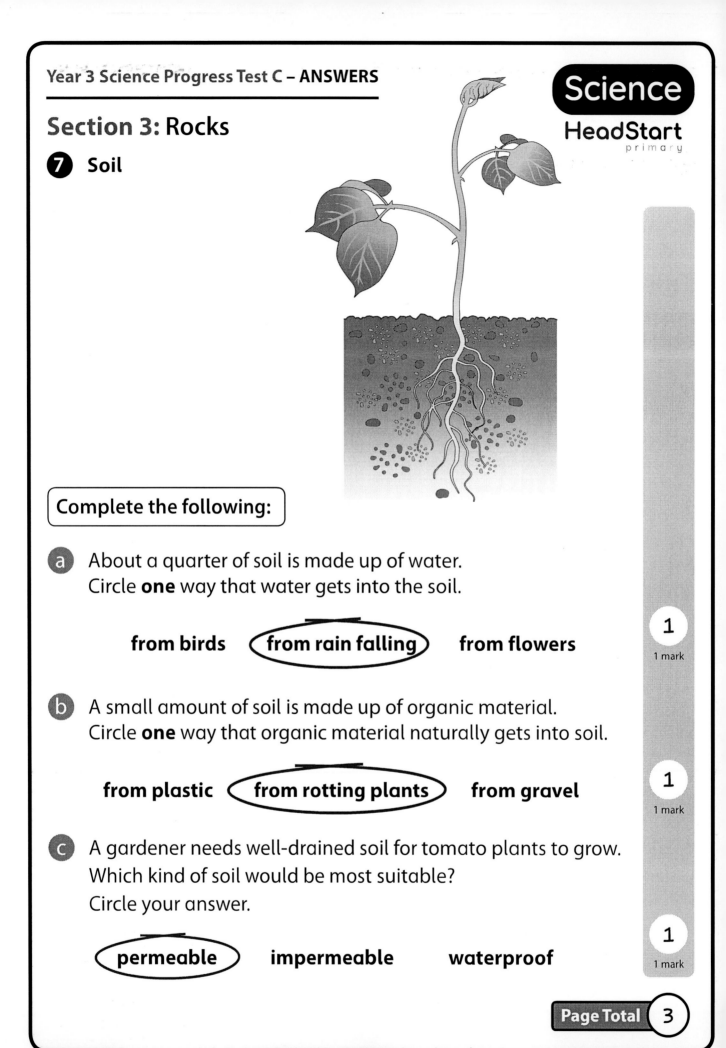

Complete the following:

a About a quarter of soil is made up of water.
Circle **one** way that water gets into the soil.

from birds   **from rain falling**   **from flowers**

1
1 mark

b A small amount of soil is made up of organic material.
Circle **one** way that organic material naturally gets into soil.

from plastic   **from rotting plants**   **from gravel**

1
1 mark

c A gardener needs well-drained soil for tomato plants to grow.
Which kind of soil would be most suitable?
Circle your answer.

permeable   **impermeable**   **waterproof**

1
1 mark

Page Total **3**

Section 3: Rocks

8 **Types of rock**

Science
HeadStart
primary

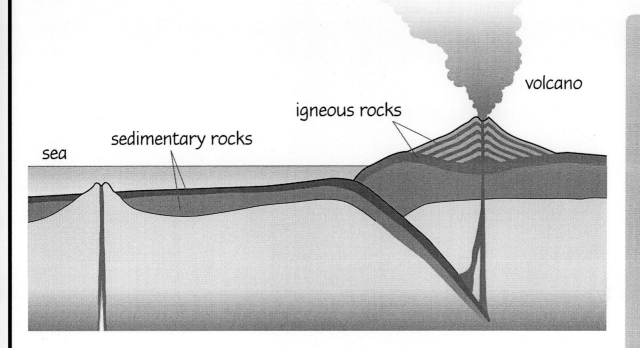

volcano

igneous rocks

sedimentary rocks

sea

Circle *true* or *false* next to the statements below:

a Igneous rock is made from layers of minerals that have settled on the sea bed over time.

true ~~false~~

b Building bricks made from clay are very permeable.

true ~~false~~

c Fossils are only formed in sedimentary rock.

~~true~~ false

d Permeable rock is suitable for the outside of buildings.

true ~~false~~

(2 marks for all 4 correct, 1 mark for 3 correct.)

2

2 marks

Page Total 2

Section 3: Rocks

9 **Fossils**

trace fossil – a footprint

body fossil – formed from the
remains of a dead animal or plant

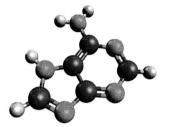

chemical fossil – chemicals
found in rocks

Circle the correct words to match the statements below:

a This kind of fossil is formed from the
remains of a dead animal or plant.

trace *(body)*

b Ancient footsteps found at low tide are
an example of this kind of fossil.

chemical *(trace)*

c You can't see this fossil but it can
be found in rocks.

(chemical) body

(2 marks for all 3 correct, 1 mark for 2 correct.)

2

2 marks

Circle *true* or *false* next to the statements below:

d It is very unlikely that fossils are found
in igneous rock.

(true) false

e Fossils can be found in rock which
formed 500 years ago.

true *(false)*

(Both must be correct for 1 mark.)

1

1 mark

Page Total **3**

© Copyright HeadStart Primary Ltd

Section 4: Light

Science
HeadStart primary

⑩ Shadows

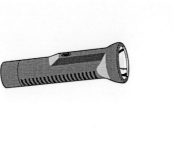

Matthias shines a torch at a clown puppet. The shadow of the puppet is seen on the wall.

Circle the correct answer to each of the following:

ⓐ What kind of material would not form a shadow?

translucent opaque **(transparent)**

1
1 mark

ⓑ What kind of material is the clown?

translucent **(opaque)** transparent

1
1 mark

ⓒ When the torch moves away from the puppet, what happens to the size of the shadow? Circle your answer.

(It gets smaller.) It gets bigger. It stays the same.

1
1 mark

ⓓ When the torch moves to the left of the puppet, what happens to the shadow? Circle your answer.

It moves left. **(It moves right.)** It stays still.

1
1 mark

Page Total **4**

Section 4: Light

⑪ Harmful or helpful sunshine?

can cause skin cancer   can provide warmth
provides us with Vitamin D
helps plants make food   causes skin to wrinkle

Complete the following:

ⓐ The Sun can be good for you and bad for you at the same time. Put the things in the box above into the correct place in the table below. Two have been done for you.

helpful (good)	harmful (bad)
provides us with vitamin D	can cause skin cancer
helps plants make food	causes skin to wrinkle
can provide warmth	

(2 marks for all 3 correct, 1 mark for 2 correct.)

2

2 marks

ⓑ Explain how you can keep your skin safe from the Sun when playing outdoors during summer months.

Answer must indicate protection of skin e.g. sun cream / clothing /shade.

1

1 mark

Page Total **3**

Section 4: Light

Science
HeadStart
primary

12 **Sources of light**

Moon

Sun

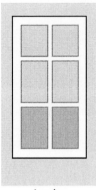

window

lamp

mirror

Complete the following:

a Which **two** of the items above are sources of light?

1 lamp ....

2 the Sun ....

2

2 marks

Circle *true* or *false* next to the statements below:

If you need to create complete darkness in a room you only need to:

b Remove all sources of light.   (true) false

c Wear sunglasses.   true (false)

(Both must be correct for 1 mark.)

1

1 mark

Page Total **3**

Section 5: Forces and magnets

13 **Everyday magnets**

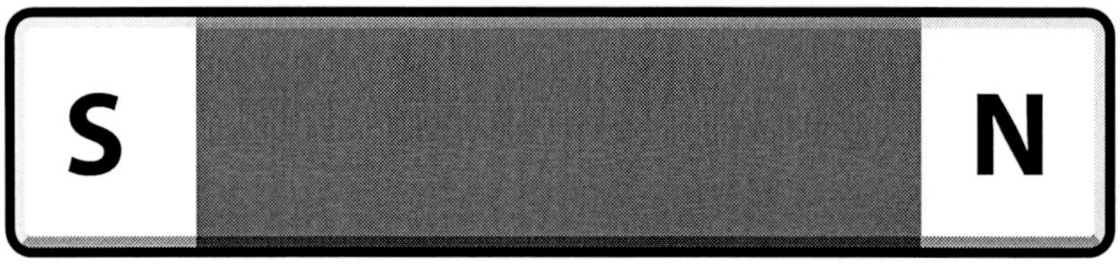

Science
HeadStart
primary

S		N

Complete the following:

a How could a magnet be used to sort items in a recycling centre?
Answer should suggest the metal items being attracted
to the magnet.

1
1 mark

b Suffaya has a magnetic picture frame. Which of the following objects will it **not** be attracted to?
Circle your answer.

fridge   (wallpaper)   radiator

1
1 mark

Write *attract* or *repel* next to each pair of magnets below:

c | S | N | | N | S | .... repel

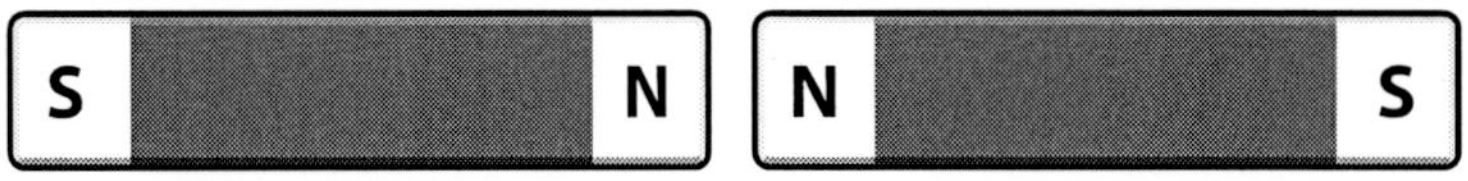

1

d | N | S | | N | S | .... attract

1
1 mark

(Both must be correct for 1 mark.)

Page Total **3**

Section 5: Forces and magnets

14 **Magnet strength**

horseshoe magnet

N   S bar magnet

button magnet

Year 3A carried out an experiment to see how strong three magnets are. The results are shown in the table below.

magnet	number of iron tacks picked up
button magnet	4
horseshoe magnet	10
bar magnet	7

Answer the following questions:

a Which magnet was the strongest?   horseshoe magnet

1
1 mark

3B were also testing the strength of different magnets. In their experiment, the horseshoe magnet picked up paper clips, the button magnet picked up drawing pins and the bar magnet picked up iron nails.

b 3B's test was not a fair test. Circle the sentence below which explains why not.

They used different magnets.

Drawing pins aren't magnetic.

1
1 mark

Each magnet picked up a different thing.

Page Total **2**

Section 5: Forces and magnets

Science
HeadStart
primary

15 **Which kind of force?**

Circle which kind of force is involved; *push* or *pull*.
Two have been done for you:

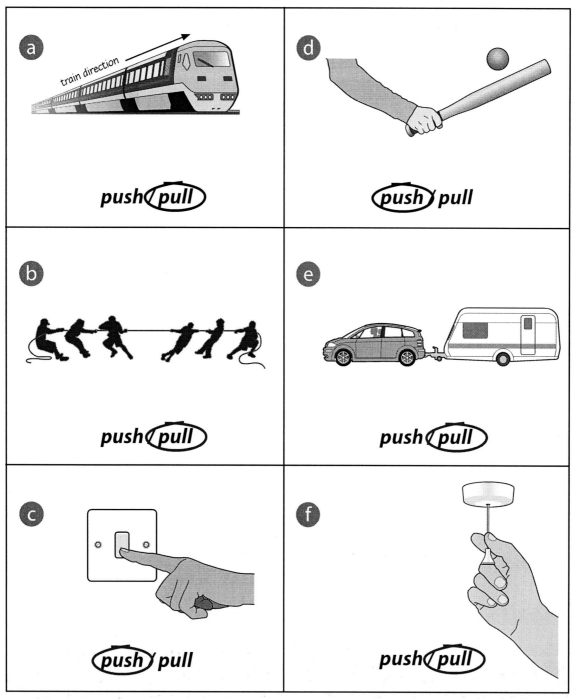

a *push* / ~~pull~~ *(pull circled)*

d ~~push~~ / *pull* *(push circled)*

b *push* / ~~pull~~ *(pull circled)*

e *push* / ~~pull~~ *(pull circled)*

c ~~push~~ / *pull* *(push circled)*

f ~~push~~ / *pull* *(push circled)*

2

2 marks

(2 marks for all 4 correct, 1 mark for 3 correct.)

Page Total 2   Test Total 44 /44

HeadStart
primary

Science

Year 3

Topic Tests

HeadStart
primary

Science

Year 3
Topic Test

Plants

Name:
....

Class:
....

Date:
....

Raw Score ....

Science

HeadStart
primary

1 **Parts of a plant**

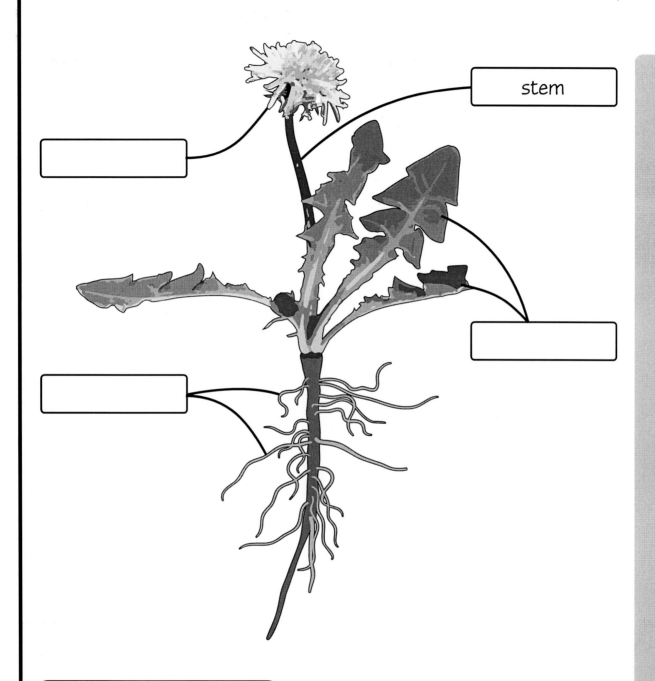

stem

Complete the following:

Write the correct part of the plant in each label.
One has been done for you.

2 marks

Page Total

Science
HeadStart
primary

2 Watering plants

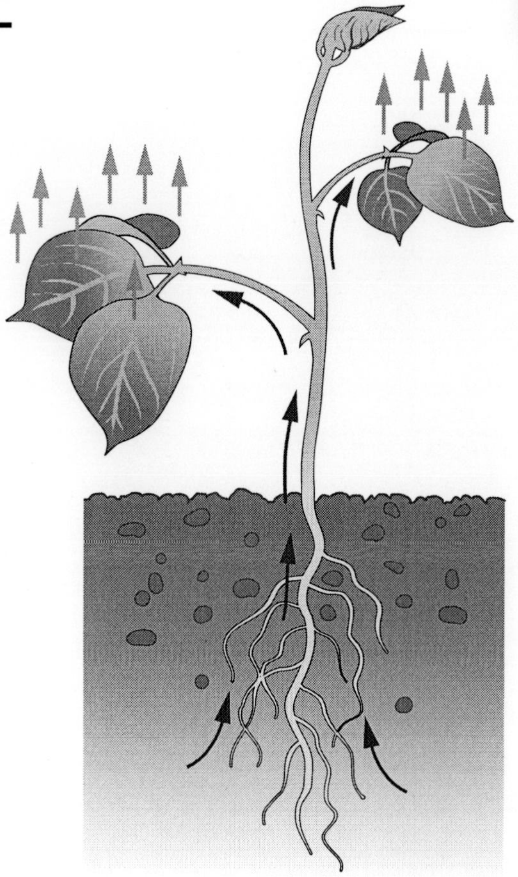

Draw lines to match each sentence to the correct part of the plant:

a Water evaporates from here.

b They collect water from the soil.

c Moves nutrients through the plant to the petals and leaves.

stem

leaves

roots

2 marks

Circle *true* or *false* next to the statements below:

d The plant gets water from the soil. ***true / false***

e Water collects in the flowers and passes down through the stem. ***true / false***

1 mark

Page Total

Science
HeadStart
p r i m a r y

3 **Plant food**

Circle *true* or *false* next to the statements below:

a The petals gather dust from the air
to feed the plant.   **true / false**

b The leaves use sunlight to create food
for the whole plant.   **true / false**

c The stem of the plant collects food from
the air.   **true / false**

2 marks

Complete the following:

d What do plants need to do to stay healthy? Circle one thing.

change colour   bend in the wind   feed

1 mark

Page Total

4 **Spreading out seeds**

conker

pea pods

dandelion

bird eating seeds

Complete the following:

a Circle **two** of the best ways that seeds can be spread out to places where plants can grow well.

falling in rain showers   **remaining on the plant**

carried on the fur of animals   **carried by the wind**

2 marks

Circle *true* or *false* next to the statements below:

b Birds eating seeds can help to spread the seeds.

true / false

c It is better for seeds to travel away from the parent plant.

true / false

1 mark

Page Total

5 **Stems**

tree trunk (stem)

pithy stem

fleshy stem

Complete the following:

a Tick **two** boxes below which describe the most important jobs of stems in plants.

☐ They carry water through the plant or tree.

☐ They are useful for putting flowers in vases.

☐ They help to keep the plant or tree upright.

☐ They are useful for small insects to climb up.

1 mark

b The flower at the top of the stem attracts bees.
Why is it important to attract bees to the flower?

....

....

1 mark

Page Total

6 **Flower head**

Circle *true* or *false* next to the statements below:

a The bright colours of the petals are attractive to insects.

true / false

b Insects land on flowers causing a lot of damage to the petals.

true / false

c Parts of the flower head produce pollen.

true / false

d The main purpose of the flower is to gather water to feed the plant.

true / false

2 marks

Page Total

⑦ Growing plants

Circle your answers to the following:

a Which **two** of the things below are most important for the growth of plants?

sunlight   wind   water   birds

2 marks

b Why does a plant need leaves to help it grow?
Circle the best answer.

They take water   They make food   They attract
from the soil.   from sunlight.   birds.

1 mark

Page Total

Science
HeadStart primary

8 **Plant experiment**

white flower

stem

water with blue food colouring added

glass vase

A white flower is cut at the stem and placed in a glass vase of water which has blue food colouring added.

Answer the following questions:

a What will happen to the white petals of the flower over time?

....   1 mark

b Why does this happen?

....

....   1 mark

Circle *true* or *false* next to the statements below:

c Roots have tiny hairs which gather water from the soil.   *true / false*

d Water is collected by the flower and moved down through the stem.   *true / false*

1 mark

Page Total

Science
HeadStart
primary

9 **Functions of parts of flowering plants**

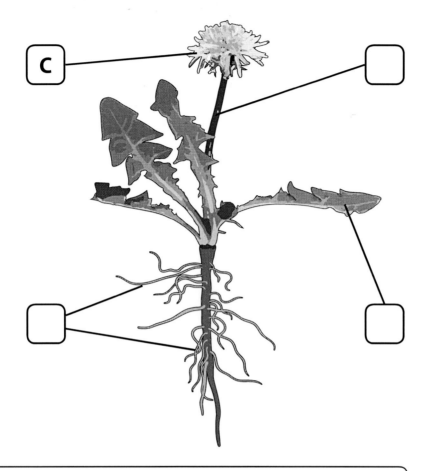

C

Look at the picture above to complete the following:

a Label the flowering plant **A**, **B**, **C** or **D** to match the statements below. One has been done for you.

A: They gather water to feed the plant.

B: Water evaporates from them.

C: Their colours are attractive to insects.

D: It helps to keep the plant upright.

2 marks

b Which part of the plant also produces sweet smells?

....

1 mark

Page Total

Test Total   /24

HeadStart
primary

Science

Year 3
Topic Test

Animals, including humans

Name:
....

Class:
....

Date:
....

Raw Score ....

1 **Human skeleton**

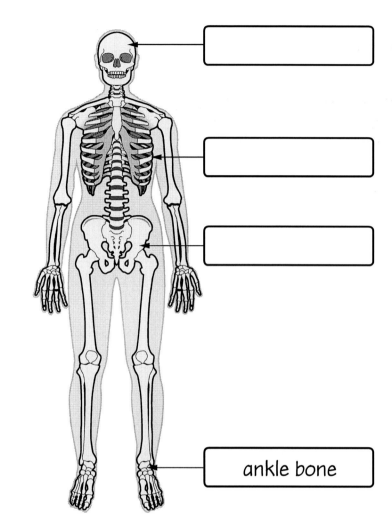

ankle bone

ribs
skull
pelvis
ankle bone

Complete the following:

a Use the words from the box above to label the bones shown in the diagram. One has been done for you.

2 marks

b Name **one** purpose of muscles in humans.

1 mark

....

Page Total

Science
HeadStart
primary

❷ Healthy diet

Circle *true* or *false* next to the statements below:

a A good human diet will include carbohydrates, proteins and fats/oils.

true / false

b Humans can get enough water each day by eating foods such as tomatoes and melon. They don't need to drink liquid water.

true / false

1 mark

Complete the following:

c Write ***pasta*** and ***cheese*** in the correct place in the table below. Two foods are already shown.

food rich in carbohydrates	food rich in fats/oils
potatoes	walnuts

1 mark

Page Total ◯

❸ Saturated and unsaturated fats

cheese

butter

DOUBLE CREAM

cream

saturated fats

olive oil

nuts

unsaturated fats

Look at the pictures above to help you complete the following:

a Which type of fat is most necessary for a healthy, balanced diet?

        saturated   **unsaturated**

1 mark

b Which of the following contains the most unsaturated fats? Circle your answer.

      biscuits   **burgers**   **fish**

1 mark

c What might happen if you eat too much unhealthy fat?

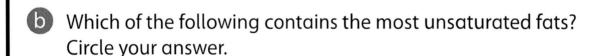

1 mark

Page Total

4 **Which is which?**

Draw lines below to match the words to the correct pictures. One has been done for you:

a thigh bone

b jaw

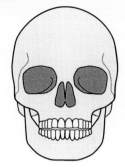

c finger bone

d skull

2 marks

Complete the following:

e Bones are necessary for movement. Give another purpose for bones.

. . . .

1 mark

Page Total

Science
HeadStart
primary

5 **Healthy food**

 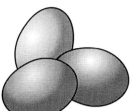  

| fruit | eggs | milk | bread |

Match the words from the box above to the descriptions below.
One has been done for you:

a provides many useful vitamins
and minerals ....fruit................

b helps to keep your teeth and
bones healthy ....

1 mark

c a good source of carbohydrates ....

1 mark

Circle *true* or *false* next to the statements below:

d Proteins help build and maintain muscles. ***true / false***

e You can eat a healthy diet by just eating
eggs and drinking milk. ***true / false***

1 mark

Page Total

6 **Types of animal skeletons**

worm

whale

crab

Circle your answer to the following:

a Which of the animals pictured above has a body with no skeleton?

worm   whale   crab

1 mark

b Some animals shed their skin several times as they grow. Which type of skeleton do these animals have?

inner skeleton   outer skeleton   no skeleton

1 mark

c Some animals have skeletons which grow with them. Which type of skeleton do these animals have?

inner skeleton   outer skeleton   no skeleton

1 mark

Page Total

7 **Bones, bones, bones!**

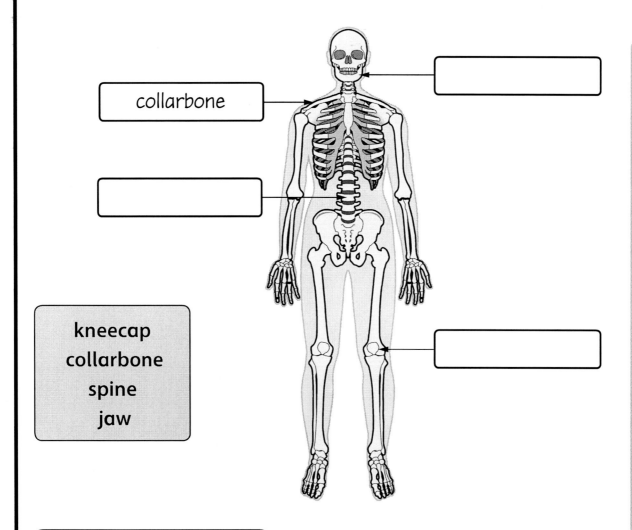

collarbone

kneecap
collarbone
spine
jaw

Complete the following:

a Use the words from the box to label the bones in the diagram.
One has been done for you.

2 marks

b Why do humans have a rib cage?

....

1 mark

Page Total

8 **Vertebrates and invertebrates**

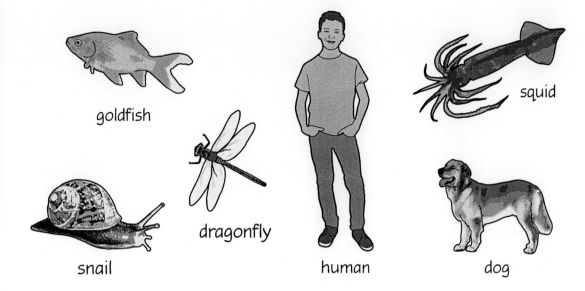

goldfish

squid

snail

dragonfly

human

dog

Look at the pictures of some vertebrates and invertebrates to help you complete the following:

a Animals with no backbone are called ....

1 mark

b Three of the living things pictured above are vertebrates. Write them in the table. One has been done for you.

vertebrates
human

2 marks

Page Total

9 **Food categories**

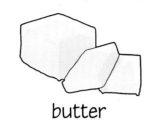

butter

apple

chips

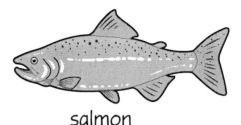

salmon

Complete the questions below:

a Which of the foods above contains the highest amount of protein?

....

1 mark

b Which of the foods above is usually made from dairy?

....

1 mark

c Chips are a source of carbohydrates.
Write one reason why we need some carbohydrates in our diet.

....

1 mark

Page Total ◯

Test Total /26

HeadStart primary

Science

Year 3 Topic Test

Rocks

Name: ....

Class: ....

Date: ....

Raw Score ....

Science

HeadStart
primary

❶ Different kinds of rock

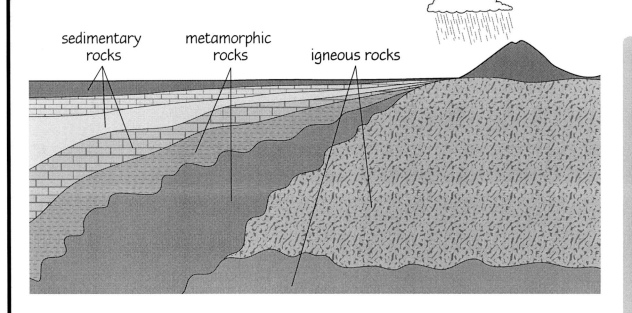

sedimentary rocks   metamorphic rocks   igneous rocks

Circle your answer to each of the following:

ⓐ Which rock is made when sedimentary or igneous rock heats up?

igneous   **sedimentary**   **metamorphic**

1 mark

ⓑ Which rock is made due to lots of heat and pressure e.g. in a volcano?

igneous   **sedimentary**   **metamorphic**

1 mark

ⓒ Man-made 'rock' can be made using material from real rock. Which of the words below is a man-made 'rock'?

igneous   **concrete**   **sedimentary**

1 mark

Page Total

2 **Rocks and fossils**

granite
(hard rock)

chalk
(soft rock)

marble
(hard-wearing rock)

Circle the correct words to match each of the sentences below:

a This rock is suitable for the outside of buildings to cope with bad weather.

marble / chalk

b This rock can be used to write with.

chalk / granite

1 mark

Circle *true* or *false* next to the statements below:

c Fossils are formed only in igneous rock.

true / false

d A fossil is the preserved impression or remains of a dead organism.

true / false

1 mark

Page Total

3 **Soil**

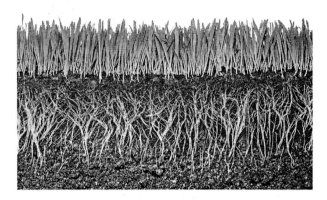

Scientists tested a sample of soil. The results were as follows:

soil is made up of	amount in soil
air	24%
water	24%
organic material	3%
minerals	49%

Answer the following questions. Use the table above to help you:

a What percentage of the soil was made up of air and water? . . . .%

1 mark

b What percentage of the soil was made up of minerals? . . . .%

1 mark

c Where could the organic material have come from? Circle your answer.

rotting plants   **sand**   **plastic bags**

1 mark

d If a type of plant grows well in well-drained soil, which soil type would be best for them? Circle your answer.

1 mark

waterproof   **permeable**   **impermeable**

Page Total

Science
HeadStart
primary

4 **Sedimentary rock**

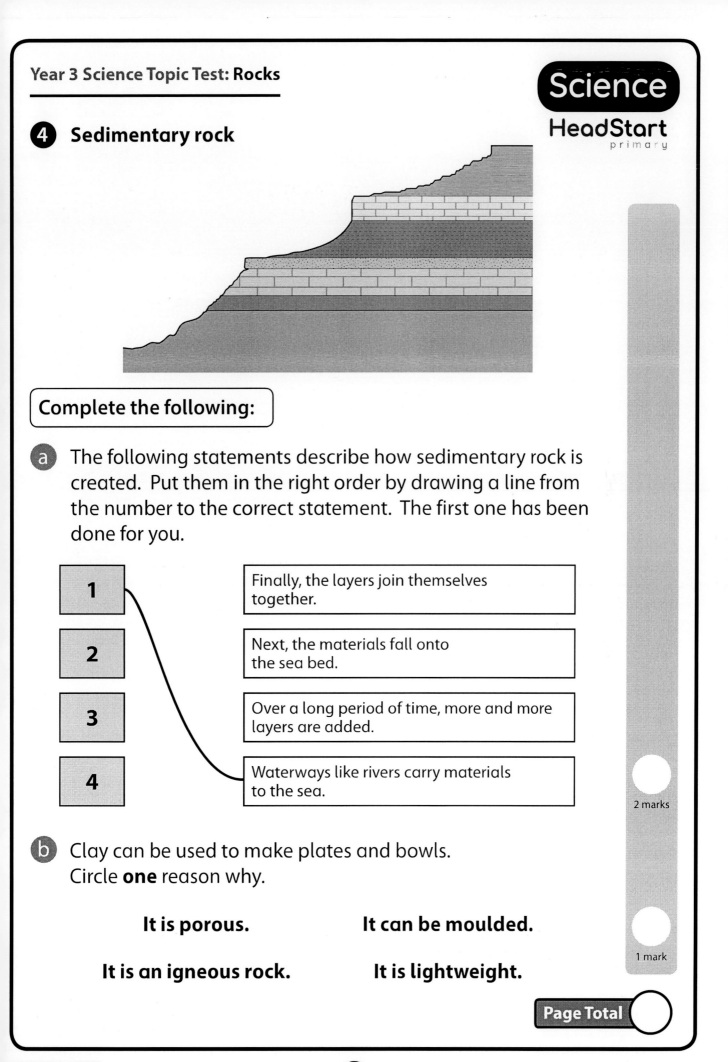

Complete the following:

a The following statements describe how sedimentary rock is created. Put them in the right order by drawing a line from the number to the correct statement. The first one has been done for you.

1	Finally, the layers join themselves together.
2	Next, the materials fall onto the sea bed.
3	Over a long period of time, more and more layers are added.
4	Waterways like rivers carry materials to the sea.

2 marks

b Clay can be used to make plates and bowls.
Circle **one** reason why.

It is porous.   **It can be moulded.**

It is an igneous rock.   **It is lightweight.**

1 mark

Page Total

⑤ Dinosaurs and fossils

Velociraptor

Pterodactyl

Tyrannosaurus

Brontosaurus

Stegosaurus

Circle *true* or *false* next to the statements below:

ⓐ Fossils of dinosaurs help us understand the
exact sounds that these extinct animals made.   ***true / false***

ⓑ Fossils can give us a clear picture of the
size of dinosaurs.   ***true / false***

ⓒ We can tell from fossils the colour of the
dinosaur's skin.   ***true / false***

ⓓ Fossils cannot be brought back to life.   ***true / false***

2 marks

Page Total

6 Creating soil

Soil can be formed in different ways. **Addition** and **loss** are two of the ways in which soil forms.

| Circle the word that matches the statement below: |

a Decaying vegetation increases the amount of soil.

addition / loss

1 mark

| Compost can improve the quality of the soil. Circle *true* or *false* next to the statements below: |

b Compost can be formed from old newspapers and plastic containers.

true / false

c Compost can be made up of decayed plant material that has rotted over a period of time.

true / false

1 mark

Page Total

7 **Types of rock**

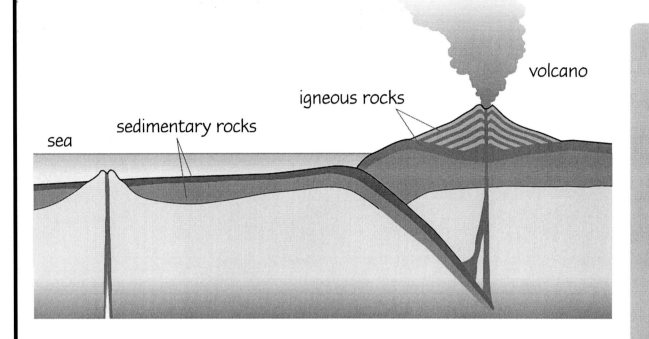

volcano

igneous rocks

sedimentary rocks

sea

Circle *true* or *false* next to the statements below:

a Igneous rock is made from layers of minerals that have settled on the sea bed over time.

true / false

b Building bricks made from clay are very permeable.

true / false

c Fossils are only formed in sedimentary rock.

true / false

d Permeable rock is suitable for the outside of buildings.

true / false

2 marks

Page Total

8 **All about soil**

Complete the following:

a About a quarter of soil is made up of water.
Circle **one** way that water gets into the soil.

from birds   **from rain falling**   **from flowers**

1 mark

Circle *true* or *false* next to the statements below:

b Organic material in soil can be made up of gravel and plastic.

true / false

c Permeable soil allows water to pass through it.

true / false

d If air gets into soil, the soil becomes unsuitable for plants.

true / false

2 marks

Page Total

Science

HeadStart
primary

9 **Fossils**

trace fossil – a footprint

body fossil – formed from the
remains of a dead animal or plant

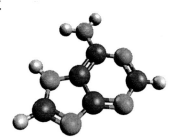

chemical fossil – chemicals
found in rocks

Circle the correct words to match the statements below:

a This kind of fossil is formed from the
remains of a dead animal or plant.

trace / body

b Ancient footsteps found at low tide are
an example of this kind of fossil.

chemical / trace

c You can't see this fossil but it can
be found in rocks.

chemical / body

2 marks

Circle *true* or *false* next to the statements below:

d The most common rock for fossils to
be found in is metamorphic rock.

true / false

e Fossils can be found in rock which
formed 500 years ago.

true / false

1 mark

Page Total

Test Total /24

9 © Copyright HeadStart Primary Ltd

HeadStart primary

Science

Year 3
Topic Test

Light

Name: ....

Class: ....

Date: ....

Raw Score ....

1 **Source or not?**

computer screen

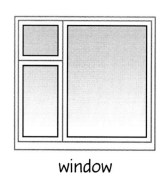

window

Sun

car headlights

Moon

Some of the objects above are light sources and some are not. Complete the table. Two have been done for you:

a

light source	not a light source
Sun	Moon

2 marks

b The Moon is not a source of light. How can it provide light on a dark night?

....

....

1 mark

Page Total

2 **Light and dark**

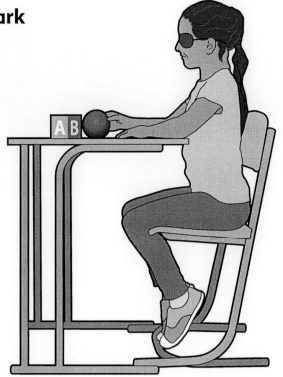

Serena is wearing a blindfold. There are objects on the table which she feels with her hands.

Circle *true* or *false* next to the statements below:

a She can tell her friends the colours of the objects.   *true / false*

b She can say how many sides the objects have.   *true / false*

c Serena can clearly see the objects.   *true / false*

2 marks

Answer the question below:

d What is the best type of material to make a blindfold from? Circle your answer.

transparent   **opaque**   **translucent**

1 mark

Page Total

© Copyright HeadStart Primary Ltd

Science

HeadStart
primary

3 **Sunlight**

| Look at the picture above and complete the following: |

a Write **one** way that the people could protect their eyes from the bright sunlight.

....

1 mark

b Write **two** ways that the people could protect their skin from the bright sunlight.

1 ....

2 ....

2 marks

c Circle **one** good thing that sunlight can do for us.

age skin   **provide vitamin D**

1 mark

keep us cool   **keep us hydrated**

Page Total

4 **Mirror, mirror, on the wall...**

Answer the following questions:

a Bobby is looking at his reflection in the mirror. He raises his left hand. Which hand appears to be raised in the mirror?

....

1 mark

b The word below appears like this in a mirror. What is the word?

ᒣOOHƆƧ

....

1 mark

c Circle the word '**HANDS**' as it would appear in a mirror.

ƧᗡᴎAH   SDИAH   HAИᗡƧ

1 mark

Page Total ◯

⑤ Light and shadow

Complete the following:

ⓐ Draw the position of the shadow in the picture above.

1 mark

Complete the following by circling the correct answer:

ⓑ The torch is moved further away from the ball.
What happens to the shadow?

The light blocks it.   **It gets smaller.**   **It gets bigger.**

1 mark

ⓒ The ball is replaced with transparent glass.
The torch remains lit and in the same position.
What happens to the shadow?

It gets smaller.   **It disappears.**   **It gets longer.**

1 mark

Page Total

Science

HeadStart
primary

6 **Letting light through**

For each of the sentences below, circle the correct word to match it:

a Curtains block out light from outside.

translucent   **opaque**   **transparent**

1 mark

b Light comes through a bathroom window, but you can't see clearly through it.

translucent   **opaque**   **transparent**

1 mark

c What kind of material would be best to use for windows looking out into the garden?

translucent   **opaque**   **transparent**

1 mark

Page Total

7 **Sources of light**

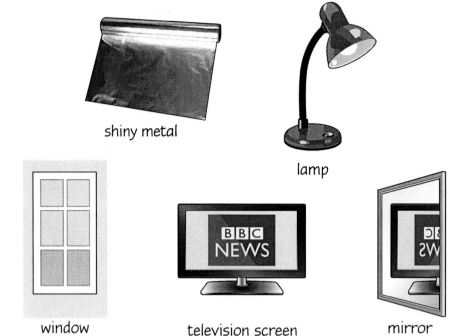

shiny metal

lamp

window

television screen

mirror

Complete the following:

a Which **two** of the items above are sources of light?

1 ....

2 ....

2 marks

Circle *true* or *false* next to the statements below:

If you need to create complete darkness in a room you only need to:

b Remove all sources of light. **true / false**

c Wear sunglasses. **true / false**

1 mark

Page Total

8 **Shadows**

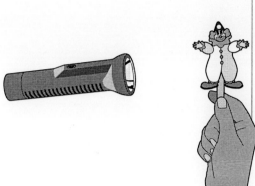

Matthias shines a torch at a clown puppet. The shadow of the puppet is seen on the wall.

> **Circle the correct answer to each of the following:**

a What kind of material would not form a shadow?

   translucent   **opaque**   **transparent**

1 mark

b What kind of material is the clown?

   translucent   **opaque**   **transparent**

1 mark

c When the torch moves nearer to the puppet, what happens to the size of the shadow? Circle your answer.

   It gets smaller.   **It gets bigger.**   **It stays the same.**

1 mark

d When the torch moves to the left of the puppet, what happens to the shadow? Circle your answer.

   It moves left.   **It moves right.**   **It stays still.**

1 mark

Page Total

⑨ **Harmful or helpful sunshine?**

can cause skin cancer	can provide warmth

provides us with Vitamin D

| helps plants make food | causes skin to wrinkle |

Complete the following:

The Sun can be good for you and bad for you at the same time.
Put the things in the box above into the correct place in the table
below. Two have been done for you.

helpful (good)	harmful (bad)
provides us with vitamin D	can cause skin cancer

2 marks

Page Total ◯   Test Total /28

HeadStart
primary

Science

Year 3
Topic Test

Forces and magnets

Name: ....

Class: ....

Date: ....

Raw Score ....

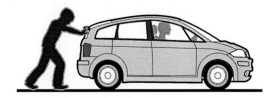

1 Magnetic material

cobalt knife

iron nail

gold ring

aluminium can

bottle

50p coin

pen

paperclip

Write the objects pictured above in the correct place in the table below. Four have been done for you:

magnetic material	non-magnetic material
cobalt knife	gold ring
50p coin	bottle

2 marks

Page Total

2 **Types of forces**

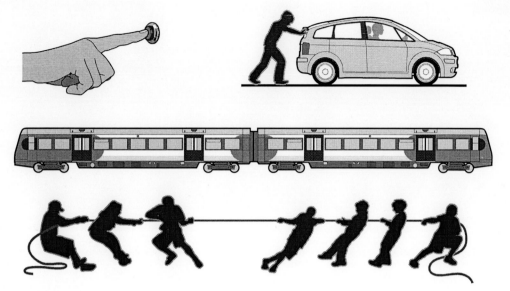

Complete the following:

a What is a force? Circle the best answer.

a strong wind   a push or pull   an earthquake

1 mark

b Tick **one** box to show a force which is being changed.

☐ increasing the brightness of a screen

☐ turning the sound up on a television

☐ pulling more tightly on bicycle brakes

1 mark

c In a tug of war, each player is of equal strength.
Team A has 3 players and team B has 4 players.
Which team will win?

....

1 mark

Page Total ◯

3 Friction experiment

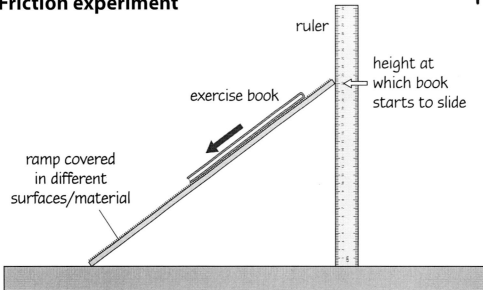

ruler

exercise book

height at
which book
starts to slide

ramp covered
in different
surfaces/material

Year 3 are testing which kind of surface creates the most friction.
An exercise book is placed on a ramp, which is lifted up until the
book starts to slide. The height is then marked.

The results are compared in the table below.

surface on ramp	height when book starts to slide
carpet	31 cm
wood	22 cm
sandpaper	45 cm

Complete the following:

a Which <u>surface</u> provided the greatest amount of friction?

....

1 mark

b Which <u>surface</u> provided the least friction?

....

1 mark

Page Total

3 **Friction experiment** (continued)

c Year 3's test was a fair test. Tick **one** reason why.

☐ The same ramp surface was used each time.

☐ The same book was used each time.

☐ A different book was used each time.

1 mark

d Friction is an important force in everyday life.
Circle **two** examples of friction.

ice freezing   hands rubbing together

the sun shining   a flower growing

a car braking   a boat floating

2 marks

Page Total

4 **Magnetism**

| N | △ | S | | S | ○ | N | right → |

Look at the magnets above and complete the following:

a How could magnet ○ be moved to the right without it being touched? Circle your answer.

Move magnet △ away from magnet ○.

Turn magnet △ the other way.

Move magnet △ towards magnet ○.

1 mark

b How could metal and plastic coins be separated without them being touched?

....

1 mark

Write *repel* or *attract* to complete each sentence below:

c A North Pole of a bar magnet will .... another North Pole.

d A South Pole of a bar magnet will .... a North Pole.

e A South Pole of a bar magnet will .... a South Pole.

2 marks

Page Total ○

5 **Faster, slower**

wood

carpet

sandpaper

Year 3 use the same amount of force to push a car along three different tracks. Each track is the same length. The children time how long it takes for the car to travel along each track.

The results are shown in the table below:

surface material	time (in seconds)
wood	2
carpet	4
sandpaper	7

Complete the following:

a What is the name of the force that slows down the car? Circle your answer.

gravity **spring** **friction** **upward**

1 mark

b Which <u>surface</u> material resulted in the car travelling fastest?

. . . .

1 mark

Page Total

5 **Faster, slower** (continued)

c Why did the car take longer on the carpet track than on the wood track? Circle the sentence below that is correct.

The carpet is warmer so the car goes slower.

Carpet creates more friction than wood.

Wood creates more friction than carpet.

1 mark

d If the sandpaper was changed to a smoother sandpaper, how long do you think the car would take?
Circle your answer.

7 seconds   **5 seconds**   **20 seconds**

1 mark

wood

carpet

sandpaper

Page Total

6 **Pedal power**

brake handle

pedals

Charlotte wants to ride her bike above along a flat road.

Complete the following:

a What force could Charlotte use on the pedals to make the bicycle travel forwards? Circle your answer.

pull **push** **twist**

1 mark

b What should Charlotte do to the brake handle to make the bicycle slow down?

....

1 mark

c As Charlotte is slowing down, a dog runs out in front of her. Explain how Charlotte could stop as quickly as possible.

....

1 mark

Page Total

7 **Everyday magnets**

S		N

Complete the following:

a How could a magnet be used to sort items in a recycling centre?

....

....

1 mark

b Suffaya has a magnetic picture frame. Which of the following objects will it **not** be attracted to?
Circle your answer.

fridge   wallpaper   radiator

1 mark

Write *attract* or *repel* next to each pair of magnets below:

c | S | N | | N | S | ....

d | N | S | | N | S | ....

1 mark

Page Total

8 **Magnet strength**

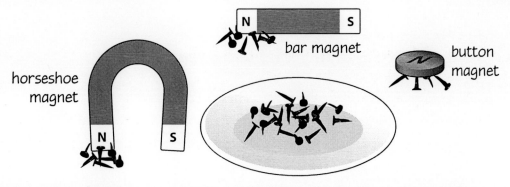

horseshoe magnet

bar magnet

button magnet

Year 3A carried out an experiment to see how strong three magnets are. The results are shown in the table below.

magnet	number of iron tacks picked up
button magnet	4
horseshoe magnet	10
bar magnet	7

Answer the following questions:

a Which magnet was the strongest? ....

1 mark

3B were also testing the strength of different magnets. In their experiment, the horseshoe magnet picked up paper clips, the button magnet picked up drawing pins and the bar magnet picked up iron nails.

b 3B's test was not a fair test. Circle the sentence below which explains why not.

They used different magnets.

Drawing pins aren't magnetic.

1 mark

Each magnet picked up a different thing.

Page Total

© Copyright HeadStart Primary Ltd

9 **Which kind of force?**

Circle which kind of force is involved; *push* or *pull*.
Two have been done for you:

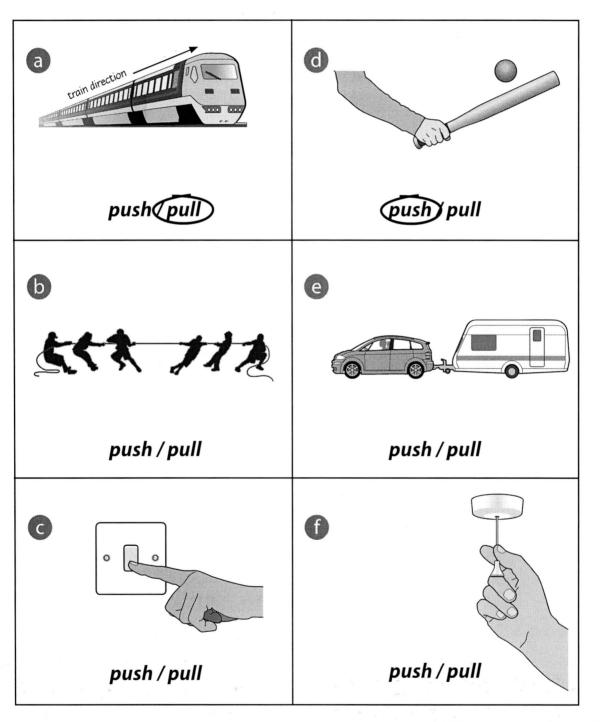

a
train direction

push / pull (pull circled)

d

push / pull (push circled)

b

push / pull

e

push / pull

c

push / pull

f

push / pull

2 marks

HeadStart
primary

Science

Year 3

Topic Tests

HeadStart
primary

Science

Year 3
Topic Test

Plants

ANSWERS

Science
HeadStart
p r i m a r y

1 **Parts of a plant**

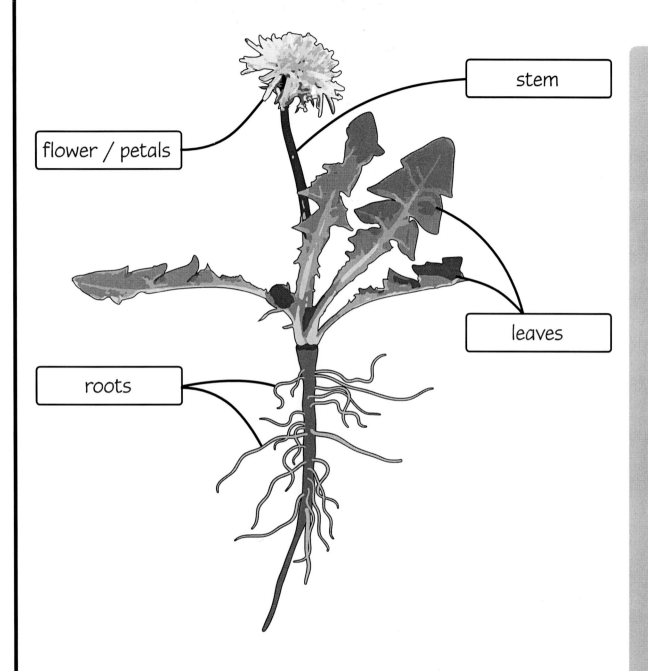

stem

flower / petals

leaves

roots

| Complete the following: |

Write the correct part of the plant in each label.
One has been done for you.

(2 marks for all 3 correct, 1 mark for 2 correct.)

2

2 marks

Page Total **2**

2 **Watering plants**

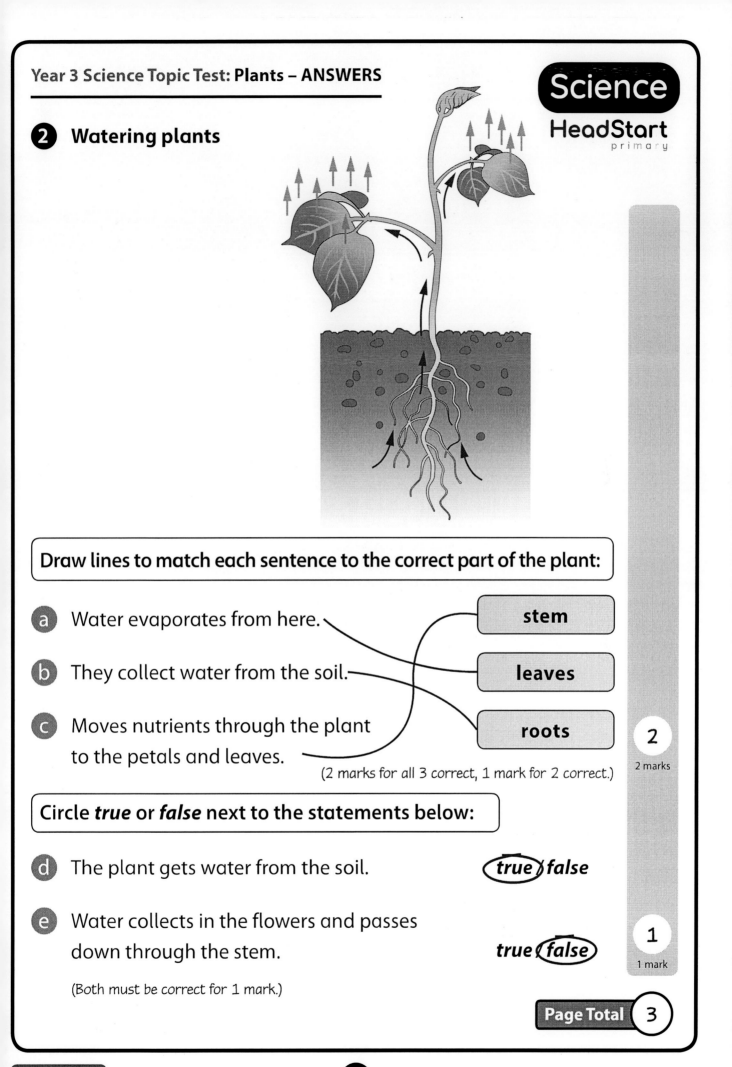

Draw lines to match each sentence to the correct part of the plant:

a Water evaporates from here.

b They collect water from the soil.

c Moves nutrients through the plant to the petals and leaves.

stem

leaves

roots

(2 marks for all 3 correct, 1 mark for 2 correct.)

2
2 marks

Circle *true* or *false* next to the statements below:

d The plant gets water from the soil.

(true) false

e Water collects in the flowers and passes down through the stem.

true (false)

(Both must be correct for 1 mark.)

1
1 mark

Page Total **3**

3 **Plant food**

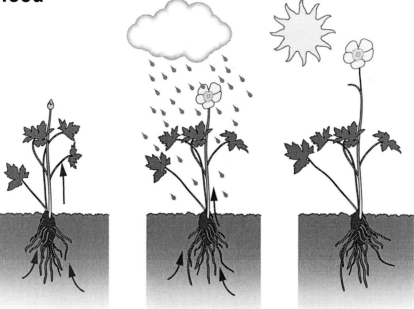

Circle *true* or *false* next to the statements below:

a The petals gather dust from the air
to feed the plant.

true (false)

b The leaves use sunlight to create food
for the whole plant.

(true) false

c The stem of the plant collects food from
the air.

true (false)

2

2 marks

(2 marks for all 3 correct, 1 mark for 2 correct.)

Complete the following:

d What do plants need to do to stay healthy? Circle one thing.

change colour   **bend in the wind**   (**feed**)

1

1 mark

Page Total **3**

4 **Spreading out seeds**

dandelion

conker

pea pods

bird eating seeds

Complete the following:

a Circle **two** of the best ways that seeds can be spread out to places where plants can grow well.

falling in rain showers   **remaining on the plant**

⟨**carried on the fur of animals**⟩   ⟨**carried by the wind**⟩   **2**

2 marks

Circle *true* or *false* next to the statements below:

b Birds eating seeds can help to spread the seeds.   ⟨true⟩ false

c It is better for seeds to travel away from the parent plant.   ⟨true⟩ false   **1**

1 mark

(Both must be correct for 1 mark.)

Page Total **3**

Science
HeadStart
primary

5 **Stems**

tree trunk (stem)   pithy stem   fleshy stem

Complete the following:

a   Tick **two** boxes below which describe the most important jobs of stems in plants.

☑ They carry water through the plant or tree.

☐ They are useful for putting flowers in vases.

☑ They help to keep the plant or tree upright.

☐ They are useful for small insects to climb up.

(Both must be correct for 1 mark.)

1
1 mark

b   The flower at the top of the stem attracts bees.
Why is it important to attract bees to the flower?

Answer should suggest bees collect pollen or nectar.

1
1 mark

Page Total **2**

6 **Flower head**

Circle *true* or *false* next to the statements below:

a The bright colours of the petals are attractive to insects.

true false

b Insects land on flowers causing a lot of damage to the petals.

true false

c Parts of the flower head produce pollen.

true false

d The main purpose of the flower is to gather water to feed the plant.

true false

(2 marks for all 4 correct, 1 mark for 3 correct.)

2

2 marks

Page Total **2**

7 **Growing plants**

Circle your answers to the following:

a Which **two** of the things below are most important for the growth of plants?

~~sunlight~~   wind    water   birds

2

2 marks

b Why does a plant need leaves to help it grow?
Circle the best answer.

They take water from the soil.   ~~They make food from sunlight.~~   They attract birds.

1

1 mark

Page Total **3**

8 **Plant experiment**

white
flower

stem

water with
blue food
colouring
added

glass vase

A white flower is cut
at the stem and placed in
a glass vase of water which
has blue food colouring added.

Answer the following questions:

a What will happen to the white petals of the flower over time?
They will turn blue.

1
1 mark

b Why does this happen?
Answer should suggest water travelling up the stem.

1
1 mark

Circle *true* or *false* next to the statements below:

c Roots have tiny hairs which gather water
from the soil.

true false

d Water is collected by the flower and
moved down through the stem.

true *false*

1
1 mark

(Both must be correct for 1 mark.)

Page Total **3**

Science
HeadStart
primary

9 **Functions of parts of flowering plants**

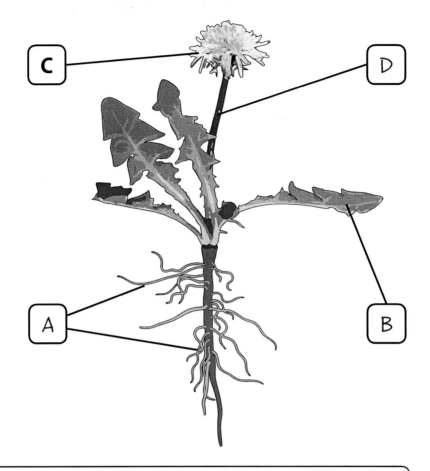

C   D

A   B

| Look at the picture above to complete the following: |

a Label the flowering plant **A**, **B**, **C** or **D** to match the statements below. One has been done for you.

A: They gather water to feed the plant.

B: Water evaporates from them.

C: Their colours are attractive to insects.

D: It helps to keep the plant upright.

(2 marks for all 3 correct, 1 mark for 2 correct.)

2

2 marks

b Which part of the plant also produces sweet smells?

flower/petals

1

1 mark

Page Total **3**   Test Total **24 /24**

HeadStart
primary

Science

Year 3
Topic Test

Animals, including humans

ANSWERS

1 **Human skeleton**

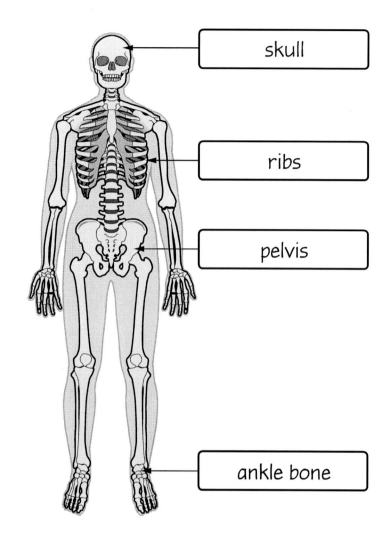

skull

ribs

pelvis

ankle bone

ribs
skull
pelvis
ankle bone

Complete the following:

a Use the words from the box above to label the bones shown in the diagram. One has been done for you.

(2 marks for all 3 correct, 1 mark for 2 correct.)

2

2 marks

b Name **one** purpose of muscles in humans.

Answer should suggest they help movement / support the skeleton.

1

1 mark

Page Total **3**

Science

HeadStart
primary

② Healthy diet

Circle *true* or *false* next to the statements below:

a A good human diet will include carbohydrates, proteins and fats/oils.

true *false*

b Humans can get enough water each day by eating foods such as tomatoes and melon. They don't need to drink liquid water.

true *false*

1
1 mark

(Both must be correct for 1 mark.)

Complete the following:

c Write ***pasta*** and ***cheese*** in the correct place in the table below. Two foods are already shown.

food rich in carbohydrates	food rich in fats/oils
potatoes	walnuts
pasta	cheese

1
1 mark

(Both must be correct for 1 mark.)

Page Total ②

Science
HeadStart
p r i m a r y

3 **Saturated and unsaturated fats**

cheese

butter

cream

saturated fats

olive oil

nuts

unsaturated fats

Look at the pictures above to help you complete the following:

a Which type of fat is most necessary for a healthy, balanced diet?

saturated   **unsaturated**

1
1 mark

b Which of the following contains the most unsaturated fats? Circle your answer.

biscuits   burgers   fish

1
1 mark

c What might happen if you eat too much unhealthy fat?
Answer should suggest an appropriate detriment to health.

1
1 mark

Page Total **3**

4 **Which is which?**

Draw lines below to match the words to the correct pictures. One has been done for you:

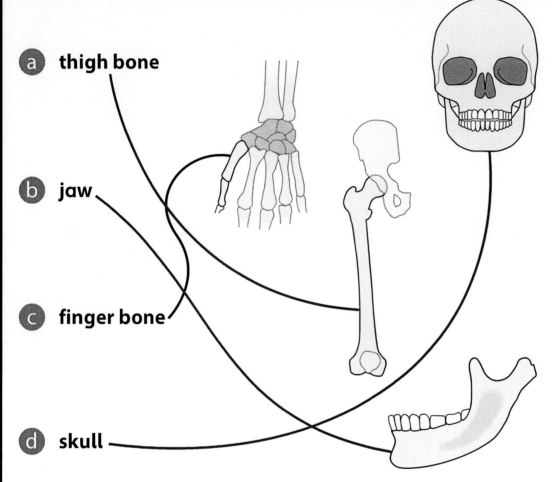

a **thigh bone**

b **jaw**

c **finger bone**

d **skull**

(2 marks for all 3 correct, 1 mark for 2 correct.)

2
2 marks

Complete the following:

e Bones are necessary for movement. Give another purpose for bones.

Answer should suggest they support the body / protect organs / allow movement.

1
1 mark

Page Total **3**

Science
HeadStart
p r i m a r y

5 **Healthy food**

 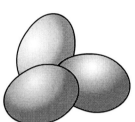  

| fruit   eggs   milk   bread |

**Match the words from the box above to the descriptions below.
One has been done for you:**

a provides many useful vitamins
and minerals

.... fruit ....

b helps to keep your teeth and
bones healthy

.... milk ....

1

1 mark

c a good source of carbohydrates

.... bread ....

1

1 mark

Circle *true* or *false* next to the statements below:

d Proteins help build and maintain muscles.

true false

e You can eat a healthy diet by just eating
eggs and drinking milk.

true **false**

1

1 mark

(Both must be correct for 1 mark.)

Page Total **3**

Science
HeadStart
p r i m a r y

6 **Types of animal skeletons**

worm

whale

crab

Circle your answer to the following:

a Which of the animals pictured above has a body with no skeleton?

~~worm~~   **whale**   **crab**

1
1 mark

b Some animals shed their skin several times as they grow. Which type of skeleton do these animals have?

inner skeleton   ~~outer skeleton~~   **no skeleton**

1
1 mark

c Some animals have skeletons which grow with them. Which type of skeleton do these animals have?

~~inner skeleton~~   **outer skeleton**   **no skeleton**

1
1 mark

Page Total **3**

Science
HeadStart
primary

7 **Bones, bones, bones!**

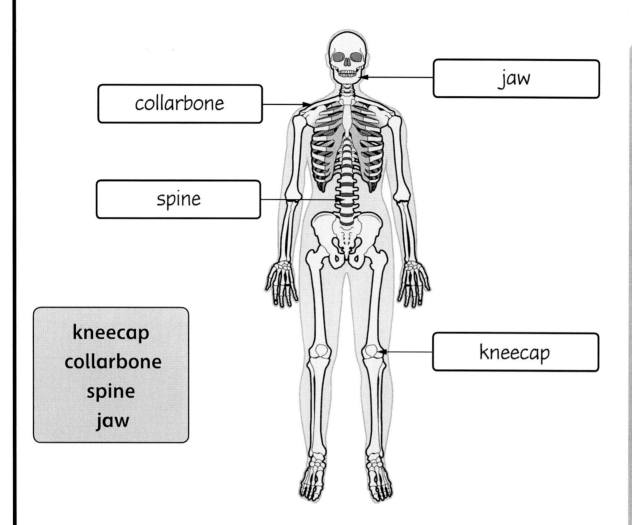

collarbone

jaw

spine

kneecap

kneecap
collarbone
spine
jaw

Complete the following:

a Use the words from the box to label the bones in the diagram. One has been done for you.

(2 marks for all 3 correct, 1 mark for 2 correct.)

2

2 marks

b Why do humans have a rib cage?

e.g. to protect the internal organs / help respiration / help support chest and back   (Accept other appropriate answers.)

1

1 mark

Page Total **3**

8 **Vertebrates and invertebrates**

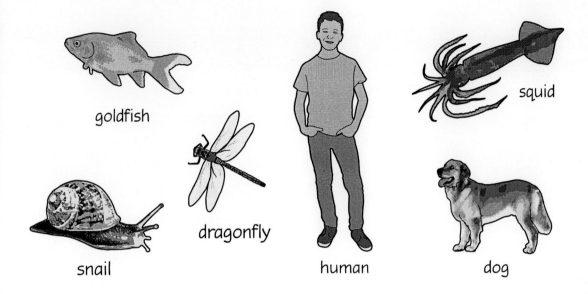

goldfish

dragonfly

squid

snail

human

dog

Look at the pictures of some vertebrates and invertebrates to help you complete the following:

a Animals with no backbone are called .... invertebrates ....

1
1 mark

b Three of the living things pictured above are vertebrates. Write them in the table. One has been done for you.

vertebrates
human
goldfish
dog

2
2 marks

Page Total **3**

Science

HeadStart
primary

9 **Food categories**

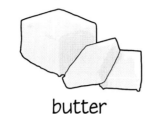

butter

apple

chips

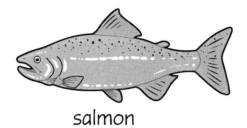

salmon

Complete the questions below:

a Which of the foods above contains the highest amount of protein?

salmon

1
1 mark

b Which of the foods above is usually made from dairy?

butter

1
1 mark

c Chips are a source of carbohydrates.
Write one reason why we need some carbohydrates in our diet.

Answer should suggest they provide energy / help build muscle / help digestion.

1
1 mark

Page Total **3**   Test Total **26 /26**

HeadStart
primary

Science

Year 3
Topic Test

Rocks

ANSWERS

1 Different kinds of rock

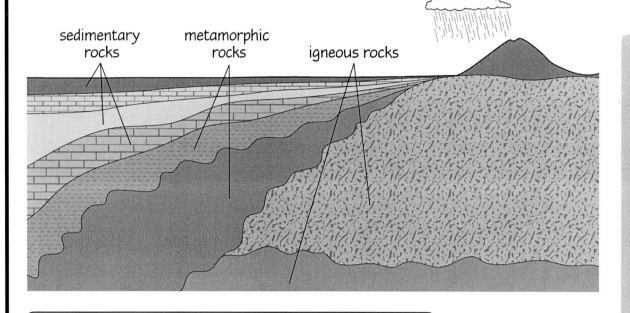

sedimentary rocks   metamorphic rocks   igneous rocks

Circle your answer to each of the following:

a Which rock is made when sedimentary or igneous rock heats up?

   igneous   **sedimentary**   (**metamorphic**)

   1
   1 mark

b Which rock is made due to lots of heat and pressure e.g. in a volcano?

   (**igneous**)   **sedimentary**   **metamorphic**

   1
   1 mark

c Man-made 'rock' can be made using material from real rock. Which of the words below is a man-made 'rock'?

   igneous   (**concrete**)   **sedimentary**

   1
   1 mark

Page Total **3**

2 Rocks and fossils

granite
(hard rock)

chalk
(soft rock)

marble
(hard-wearing rock)

Circle the correct words to match each of the sentences below:

a This rock is suitable for the outside of buildings to cope with bad weather.

(marble) chalk

b This rock can be used to write with.

(chalk) granite

1

1 mark

(Both must be correct for 1 mark.)

Circle *true* or *false* next to the statements below:

c Fossils are formed only in igneous rock.

true (false)

d A fossil is the preserved impression or remains of a dead organism.

(true) false

1

1 mark

(Both must be correct for 1 mark.)

Page Total 2

3 Soil

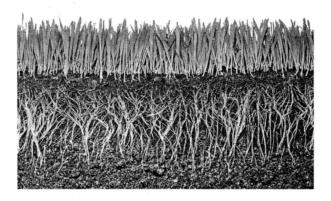

Scientists tested a sample of soil. The results were as follows:

soil is made up of	amount in soil
air	24%
water	24%
organic material	3%
minerals	49%

Answer the following questions. Use the table above to help you:

a What percentage of the soil was
made up of air and water? .... 48 ....%

1
1 mark

b What percentage of the soil was
made up of minerals? .... 49 ....%

1
1 mark

c Where could the organic material have come from?
Circle your answer.

(rotting plants)   **sand**   **plastic bags**

1
1 mark

d If a type of plant grows well in well-drained soil, which soil
type would be best for them? Circle your answer.

waterproof   (**permeable**)   **impermeable**

1
1 mark

Page Total **4**

Science
HeadStart
primary

4 **Sedimentary rock**

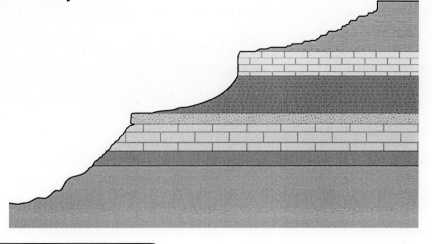

Complete the following:

a The following statements describe how sedimentary rock is created. Put them in the right order by drawing a line from the number to the correct statement. The first one has been done for you.

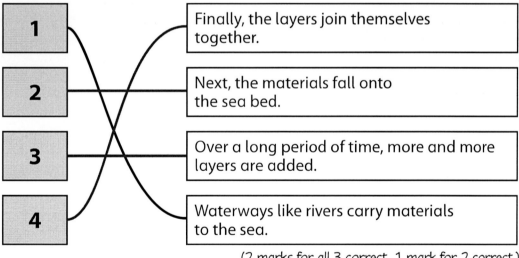

1	Finally, the layers join themselves together.
2	Next, the materials fall onto the sea bed.
3	Over a long period of time, more and more layers are added.
4	Waterways like rivers carry materials to the sea.

(2 marks for all 3 correct, 1 mark for 2 correct.)

2

2 marks

b Clay can be used to make plates and bowls.
Circle **one** reason why.

It is porous.   It can be moulded.

It is an igneous rock.   It is lightweight.

1

1 mark

Page Total **3**

⑤ Dinosaurs and fossils

Velociraptor

Pterodactyl

Tyrannosaurus

Brontosaurus

Stegosaurus

Circle *true* or *false* next to the statements below:

a Fossils of dinosaurs help us understand the
exact sounds that these extinct animals made.

true ~~*false*~~

b Fossils can give us a clear picture of the
size of dinosaurs.

~~*true*~~ *false*

c We can tell from fossils the colour of the
dinosaur's skin.

true ~~*false*~~

d Fossils cannot be brought back to life.

~~*true*~~ *false*

(2 marks for all 4 correct, 1 mark for 3 correct.)

2

2 marks

Page Total ② 2

6 **Creating soil**

Soil can be formed in different ways. **Addition** and **loss** are two of the ways in which soil forms.

> **Circle the word that matches the statement below:**

a Decaying vegetation increases the amount of soil.

1
1 mark

> **Compost can improve the quality of the soil.**
> **Circle *true* or *false* next to the statements below:**

b Compost can be formed from old newspapers and plastic containers.

c Compost can be made up of decayed plant material that has rotted over a period of time.

1
1 mark

(Both must be correct for 1 mark.)

Page Total **2**

7 **Types of rock**

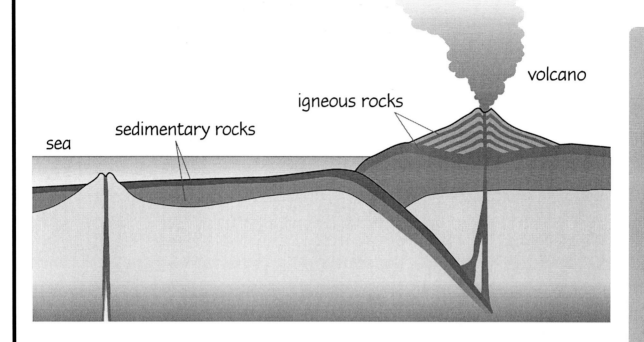

Circle *true* or *false* next to the statements below:

a Igneous rock is made from layers of minerals that have settled on the sea bed over time.

true (false)

b Building bricks made from clay are very permeable.

true (false)

c Fossils are only formed in sedimentary rock.

(true) false

d Permeable rock is suitable for the outside of buildings.

true (false)

2

2 marks

(2 marks for all 4 correct, 1 mark for 3 correct.)

Page Total **2**

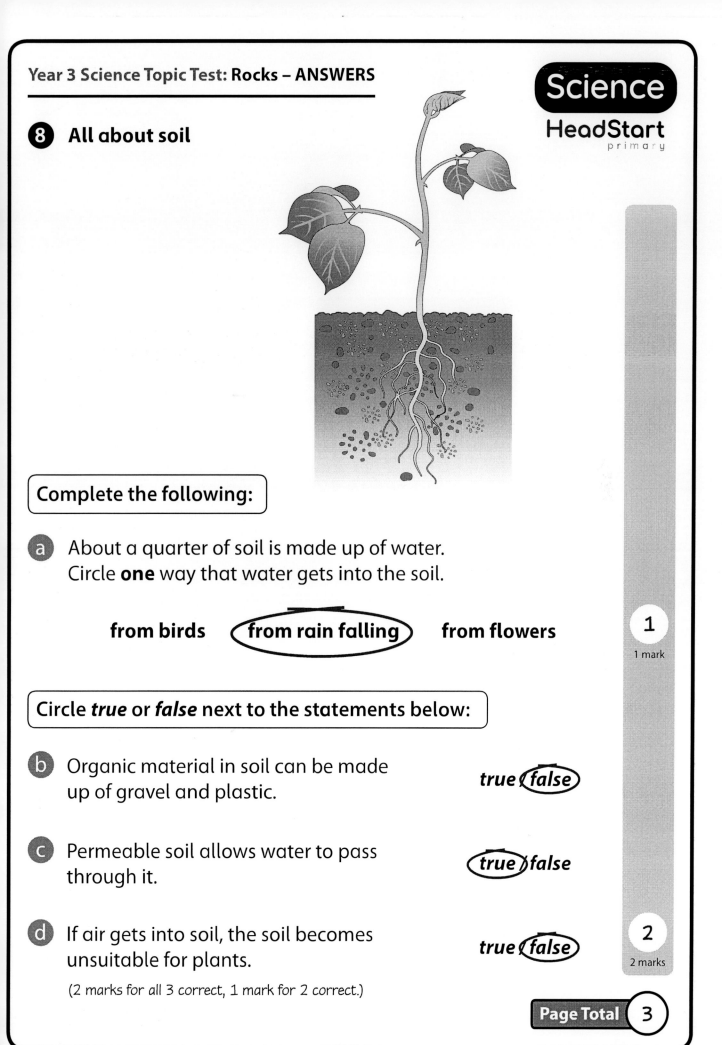

8 All about soil

Complete the following:

a About a quarter of soil is made up of water.
Circle **one** way that water gets into the soil.

from birds   (**from rain falling**)   **from flowers**

1
1 mark

Circle *true* or *false* next to the statements below:

b Organic material in soil can be made
up of gravel and plastic.

true (*false*)

c Permeable soil allows water to pass
through it.

(*true*) false

d If air gets into soil, the soil becomes
unsuitable for plants.

true (*false*)

2
2 marks

(2 marks for all 3 correct, 1 mark for 2 correct.)

Page Total **3**

9 **Fossils**

trace fossil – a footprint

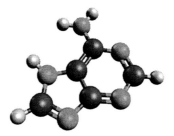

body fossil – formed from the
remains of a dead animal or plant

chemical fossil – chemicals
found in rocks

Circle the correct words to match the statements below:

a This kind of fossil is formed from the
remains of a dead animal or plant.

trace *(body)*

b Ancient footsteps found at low tide are
an example of this kind of fossil.

chemical *(trace)*

c You can't see this fossil but it can
be found in rocks.

(chemical) body

(2 marks for all 3 correct, 1 mark for 2 correct.)

2

2 marks

Circle *true* or *false* next to the statements below:

d The most common rock for fossils to
be found in is metamorphic rock.

true *(false)*

e Fossils can be found in rock which
formed 500 years ago.

true *(false)*

(Both must be correct for 1 mark.)

1

1 mark

Page Total **3**   Test Total **24 /24**

HeadStart
primary

Science

Year 3
Topic Test

Light

ANSWERS

① Source or not?

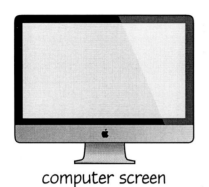

computer screen

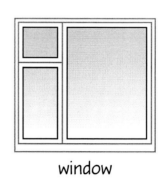

window

Sun

car headlights

Moon

Some of the objects above are light sources and some are not. Complete the table. Two have been done for you:

a

light source	not a light source
Sun	Moon
car headlights	window
computer screen	

(2 marks for all 3 correct, 1 mark for 2 correct.)

2

2 marks

b The Moon is not a source of light. How can it provide light on a dark night?

Answer should suggest it reflects light from the Sun.

1

1 mark

Page Total ③

2 Light and dark

Serena is wearing a blindfold. There are objects on the table which she feels with her hands.

Circle *true* or *false* next to the statements below:

a She can tell her friends the colours of the objects.   *true* (*false*)

b She can say how many sides the objects have.   (*true*) *false*

c Serena can clearly see the objects.   *true* (*false*)

(2 marks for all 3 correct, 1 mark for 2 correct.)

2

2 marks

Answer the question below:

d What is the best type of material to make a blindfold from? Circle your answer.

transparent   (**opaque**)   **translucent**

1

1 mark

Page Total **3**

Science
HeadStart
primary

3 **Sunlight**

Look at the picture above and complete the following:

a Write **one** way that the people could protect their eyes from the bright sunlight.

Answer should suggest protection of eyes e.g. wearing sunglasses / peaked cap.

1
1 mark

b Write **two** ways that the people could protect their skin from the bright sunlight.

1 Answer should suggest protection of skin

2 e.g. suncream / clothing / shade.

2
2 marks

c Circle **one** good thing that sunlight can do for us.

age skin   (provide vitamin D)

keep us cool   keep us hydrated

1
1 mark

Page Total **4**

4 **Mirror, mirror, on the wall...**

Answer the following questions:

a Bobby is looking at his reflection in the mirror. He raises his left hand. Which hand appears to be raised in the mirror?

right hand

1
1 mark

b The word below appears like this in a mirror. What is the word?

ꙄⅼOOHϽꙄ   SCHOOL

1
1 mark

c Circle the word '**HANDS**' as it would appear in a mirror.

(ꙄⅮИAH)   **SDNAH**   **HAИⅭꙄ**

1
1 mark

⑤ Light and shadow

shadow drawn in appropriate position

| **Complete the following:** |

ⓐ Draw the position of the shadow in the picture above.
Accept an appropriate position of the shadow.

1
1 mark

| **Complete the following by circling the correct answer:** |

ⓑ The torch is moved further away from the ball.
What happens to the shadow?

The light blocks it. 　　 It gets smaller. 　　 **It gets bigger.**

1
1 mark

ⓒ The ball is replaced with transparent glass.
The torch remains lit and in the same position.
What happens to the shadow?

It gets smaller. 　　 It disappears. 　　 **It gets longer.**

1
1 mark

Page Total ③

6 **Letting light through**

For each of the sentences below, circle the correct word to match it:

a Curtains block out light from outside.

translucent   ⟨opaque⟩   transparent

1
1 mark

b Light comes through a bathroom window, but you can't see clearly through it.

⟨translucent⟩   opaque   transparent

1
1 mark

c What kind of material would be best to use for windows looking out into the garden?

translucent   opaque   ⟨transparent⟩

1
1 mark

Page Total **3**

Science
HeadStart
p r i m a r y

7 **Sources of light**

shiny metal

lamp

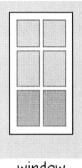
window

television screen

mirror

Complete the following:

a Which **two** of the items above are sources of light?

1 ....lamp.....................................

2 ....television screen..........................

2

2 marks

Circle *true* or *false* next to the statements below:

If you need to create complete darkness in a room you only need to:

b Remove all sources of light.
true *false*

c Wear sunglasses.
true *false*

(Both must be correct for 1 mark.)

1

1 mark

Page Total 3

⑧ Shadows

Matthias shines a torch at a clown puppet. The shadow of the puppet is seen on the wall.

Circle the correct answer to each of the following:

ⓐ What kind of material would not form a shadow?

translucent   opaque   **(transparent)**

1
1 mark

ⓑ What kind of material is the clown?

translucent   **(opaque)**   transparent

1
1 mark

ⓒ When the torch moves nearer to the puppet, what happens to the size of the shadow? Circle your answer.

It gets smaller.   **(It gets bigger.)**   It stays the same.

1
1 mark

ⓓ When the torch moves to the left of the puppet, what happens to the shadow? Circle your answer.

It moves left.   **(It moves right.)**   It stays still.

1
1 mark

Page Total **4**

Science
HeadStart
primary

9 **Harmful or helpful sunshine?**

can cause skin cancer	can provide warmth
provides us with Vitamin D	
helps plants make food	causes skin to wrinkle

Complete the following:

The Sun can be good for you and bad for you at the same time. Put the things in the box above into the correct place in the table below. Two have been done for you.

helpful (good)	harmful (bad)
provides us with vitamin D	can cause skin cancer
helps plants make food	causes skin to wrinkle
can provide warmth	

(2 marks for all 3 correct, 1 mark for 2 correct.)

2
2 marks

Page Total ⓶   Test Total 28 /28

HeadStart
primary

Science

Year 3
Topic Test

Forces and magnets

ANSWERS

Science
HeadStart
primary

1 Magnetic material

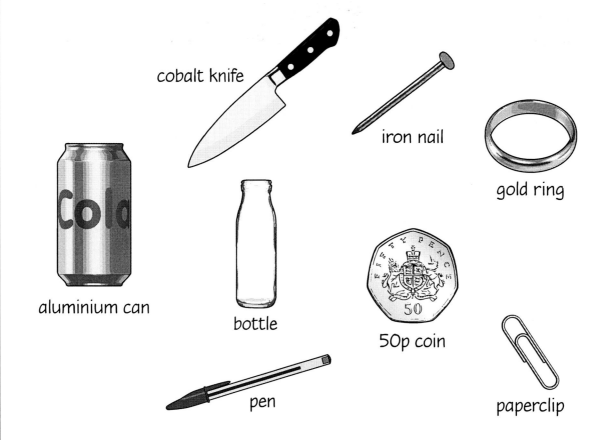

cobalt knife

iron nail

gold ring

aluminium can

bottle

50p coin

pen

paperclip

Write the objects pictured above in the correct place in the table below. Four have been done for you:

magnetic material	non-magnetic material
cobalt knife	gold ring
50p coin	bottle
paper clip	pen
iron nail	aluminium can

2

2 marks

(2 marks for all 4 correct, 1 mark for 3 correct.)

Page Total ② 2

2 Types of forces

Complete the following:

a What is a force? Circle the best answer.

a strong wind   (a push or pull)   an earthquake

1
1 mark

b Tick **one** box to show a force which is being changed.

☐ increasing the brightness of a screen

☐ turning the sound up on a television

☑ pulling more tightly on bicycle brakes

1
1 mark

c In a tug of war, each player is of equal strength.
Team A has 3 players and team B has 4 players.
Which team will win?

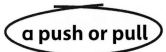

.... Team B ....

1
1 mark

Page Total 3

③ Friction experiment

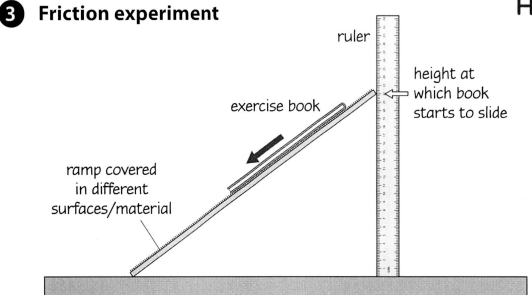

Year 3 are testing which kind of surface creates the most friction. An exercise book is placed on a ramp, which is lifted up until the book starts to slide. The height is then marked.

The results are compared in the table below.

surface on ramp	height when book starts to slide
carpet	31 cm
wood	22 cm
sandpaper	45 cm

Complete the following:

a Which <u>surface</u> provided the greatest amount of friction?

.... *sandpaper* ....

1

1 mark

b Which <u>surface</u> provided the least friction?

.... *wood* ....

1

1 mark

Page Total ② 2

Science
HeadStart
p r i m a r y

3 **Friction experiment** (continued)

c Year 3's test was a fair test. Tick **one** reason why.

☐ The same ramp surface was used each time.

☑ The same book was used each time.

☐ A different book was used each time.

1
1 mark

d Friction is an important force in everyday life.
Circle **two** examples of friction.

ice freezing   ⟨hands rubbing together⟩

the sun shining   a flower growing

⟨a car braking⟩   a boat floating

2
2 marks

Page Total **3**

4 **Magnetism**

| N | ▲ | S | | S | ● | N | → right |

Look at the magnets above and complete the following:

a How could magnet ◯ be moved to the right without it being touched? Circle your answer.

Move magnet △ away from magnet ◯.

Turn magnet △ the other way.

Move magnet △ towards magnet ◯.

1
1 mark

b How could metal and plastic coins be separated without them being touched?

Use a magnet.

1
1 mark

Write *repel* or *attract* to complete each sentence below:

c A North Pole of a bar magnet will ......*repel*...... another North Pole.

d A South Pole of a bar magnet will ......*attract*...... a North Pole.

2
2 marks

e A South Pole of a bar magnet will ......*repel*...... a South Pole.

(2 marks for all 3 correct, 1 mark for 2 correct.)

Page Total **4**

5 **Faster, slower**

wood

carpet

sandpaper

Year 3 use the same amount of force to push a car along three different tracks. Each track is the same length. The children time how long it takes for the car to travel along each track.

The results are shown in the table below:

surface material	time (in seconds)
wood	2
carpet	4
sandpaper	7

Complete the following:

a   What is the name of the force that slows down the car? Circle your answer.

gravity   **spring**   (**friction**)   **upward**

1
1 mark

b   Which <u>surface</u> material resulted in the car travelling fastest?

......................*wood*..

1
1 mark

Page Total 2

⑤ Faster, slower (continued)

Ⓒ Why did the car take longer on the carpet track than on the wood track? Circle the sentence below that is correct.

The carpet is warmer so the car goes slower.

❰Carpet creates more friction than wood.❱

Wood creates more friction than carpet.

1
1 mark

Ⓓ If the sandpaper was changed to a smoother sandpaper, how long do you think the car would take?
Circle your answer.

7 seconds  **5 seconds** **20 seconds**

1
1 mark

wood

carpet

sandpaper

Page Total ②

6 Pedal power

brake handle

pedals

Charlotte wants to ride her bike above along a flat road.

Complete the following:

a What force could Charlotte use on the pedals to make the bicycle travel forwards? Circle your answer.

pull push twist

1

1 mark

b What should Charlotte do to the brake handle to make the bicycle slow down?

Answer should indicate pulling the handle.

1

1 mark

c As Charlotte is slowing down, a dog runs out in front of her. Explain how Charlotte could stop as quickly as possible.

Answer should suggest increasing the friction
e.g. pulling brake harder / putting feet down

1

1 mark

Page Total 3

7 Everyday magnets

| S | | N |

Complete the following:

a How could a magnet be used to sort items in a recycling centre?
Answer should suggest the metal items being attracted to
the magnet.

1
1 mark

b Suffaya has a magnetic picture frame. Which of the following objects will it **not** be attracted to?
Circle your answer.

fridge      radiator

1
1 mark

Write *attract* or *repel* next to each pair of magnets below:

c | S | N | | N | S | repel

d | N | S | | N | S | attract

1
1 mark

(Both must be correct for 1 mark.)

Page Total **3**

Science
HeadStart
primary

8 **Magnet strength**

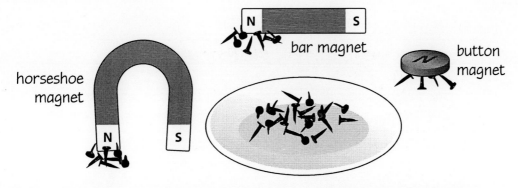

horseshoe magnet

bar magnet

button magnet

Year 3A carried out an experiment to see how strong three magnets are. The results are shown in the table below.

magnet	number of iron tacks picked up
button magnet	4
horseshoe magnet	10
bar magnet	7

Answer the following questions:

a Which magnet was the strongest? ....horseshoe magnet.......

1

1 mark

3B were also testing the strength of different magnets. In their experiment, the horseshoe magnet picked up paper clips, the button magnet picked up drawing pins and the bar magnet picked up iron nails.

b 3B's test was not a fair test. Circle the sentence below which explains why not.

They used different magnets.

Drawing pins aren't magnetic.

1

1 mark

Each magnet picked up a different thing.

Page Total 2

9 **Which kind of force?**

Circle which kind of force is involved; *push* or *pull*.
Two have been done for you:

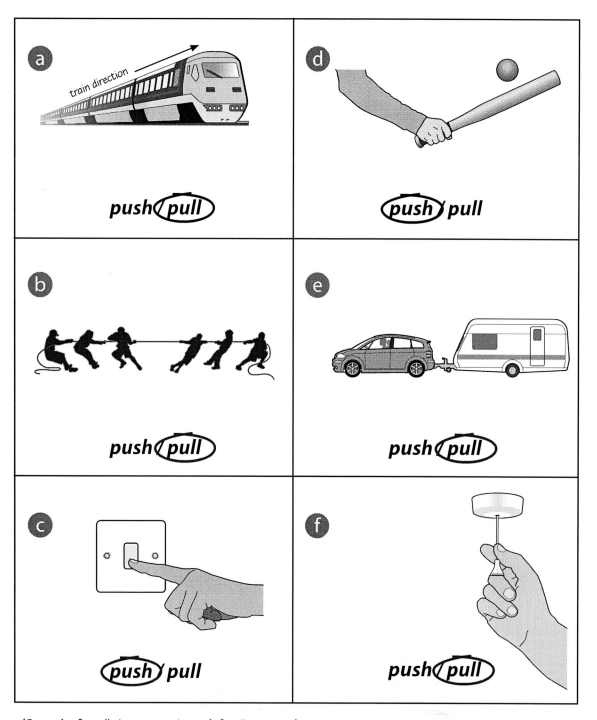

(2 marks for all 4 correct, 1 mark for 3 correct.)

Page Total 2   Test Total 28/28

PLEASE NOTE:

The CD-ROM/digital version contains the tests filed separately for printing.
Colour versions of the tests are included on the digital version.

Also supplied on the CD-ROM/digital version:

- **National curriculum links for each Progress Test**

- **National curriculum links for each Topic Test**

- **Scaled score conversion tables for each Progress Test**

- **Standardisation tables for each Topic Test**